Seeing Near and Seeing Far
The Story of Microscopes and Telescopes

Since his beginnings, man has been trying to increase the powers of perception that his five senses offer him. Perhaps his greatest strides, his greatest extension beyond the limits of nature, are in the area of vision. Mr. Ludovici explores the origins and the history of the microscope and the telescope. He discusses the great scientists remembered for their tremendous contributions to the development of these two instruments, men such as Huygens, Newton, Hooke, Kepler, Röntgen, and Koch.

A SCIENCE SURVEY BOOK

Seeing Near and Seeing Far

The Story of Microscopes and Telescopes

By L. J. LUDOVICI

Illustrated by Raymonde Ludovici

G.P. Putnam's Sons New York

For Tommy and Dorothy,
taking us back to Oxford days,
and all the memories since . . .

Published simultaneously in the Dominion of
Canada by Longmans Canada Limited, Toronto
Library of Congress Catalog Card Number:
AC 67-10150
PRINTED IN THE
UNITED STATES OF AMERICA
12216

Contents

Part One
Man Yearns to Extend His Vision
Page 9

Part Two
Men of Science Conquer New Worlds
Page 48

Part Three
Leeuwenhoek Explores a World Once Unseen
Page 106

Part Four
Astrology Yields to Science
Page 127

By the same author:

FLEMING: DISCOVERER OF PENICILLIN

THE DISCOVERY OF ANAESTHESIA: THE STRANGE STORY OF THE ETHER CONTROVERSY

GREAT MOMENTS IN MEDICINE

LOOKING AT LANGUAGES

THE WORLD OF THE MICROSCOPE

LINKS OF LIFE

THE GREAT TREE OF LIFE

Author's Note

This book, SEEING NEAR AND SEEING FAR, deals chiefly with the technical developments that offered science (astronomy and biology in particular), its means of discovery.

Its discoveries, and their discoverers, I have treated more fully in my *World of the Microscope* (microbiology), *Links of Life* (genetics and molecular biology), and *The Great Tree of Life* (anthropology and paleontology), which should, therefore, be read as companion volumes.

Man Yearns to Extend His Vision

Part One: I

LEGEND has it that when Julius Caesar wanted to invade Britain he had put up on the coast of Gaul a system of great reflecting mirrors that enabled him to watch every movement of the Britons within their towns and fortresses. Other legends tell how the ancients set fire to enemy ships and cities by directing the sun's rays at them through huge burning glasses. Such tall stories reflect Man's yearning to surpass the powers with which nature endowed him. One of his earliest successes was the spear. By devising the spear he extended the power of his muscles. Instead of having to chase and capture animals he needed to kill for food he could hurl his spear at them from a distance with good chance of success. Instead of taking part in dangerous hand-to-hand combat with human foes he could likewise assail them from afar with less risk to himself. As Professor J. D.

Bernal has stated "Viewed in the perspective of evolutionary history, science marks a conscious elaboration of the experience provided by sensory and motor organs of the body." In other words Man has kept trying to increase the number of feats he can perform by means of the complex motions he is able to command of his body. Equally he keeps trying to increase the powers of perception that his five senses offer him.

In his earliest days, Man's chief concern was to make himself safer from the dangers threatening him in the world outside the somber caves that were his refuge: wild animals on the prowl, extremes of heat and cold, rains, floods, thunder, lightning, tempests, and diseases. Having recognized the problem to be solved, early Man used his imagination and experimented in the light of his observations. In his simple way he did what scientists are still doing. He classified, he measured, he discovered new relationships between things. To make a spear he had first to invent an instrument with which to carve it. The hand-ax was his basic tool.

In the development and refinement of the hand-ax we read the development of human civilization itself. With the hand-ax he carved a spear to the shape, size, and weight that suited him. He took into account the grip of the hand, the strength of the arm. He ensured proper balance and the best path of flight through the air in order to secure both accuracy and penetrating power. The resolution of such delicate and complicated matters could not have been easy until he accounted separately (by *analysis*) for each of the many factors with which he had to deal. He then had to put all the factors together (*synthesis*) in order to create the whole, the final product, which had to work. Doubtless he spent hours of trial and error before at last succeeding.

Man taught himself to paint marvelously on the walls of caves, to carve figures out of stone and wood; at the same time he taught himself to make spears and other such equipment. Thus he was, from the very start, both artist and scientist.

To extend his power of hearing Man probably cupped a hand to his ear or used some conveniently shaped object as an ear trumpet. To extend his power of voice he probably made a megaphone with his hands and shouted through them, paying due attention to the direction of the wind.

To extend his power of vision was, however, far more difficult. He probably taught himself to shade his eyes with his hands in order the better to discern objects remote or obscured by strong glare. He probably noted day and night shadows and understood how his own eyesight varied under different conditions of light. He thus became aware of certain principles of light, and of vision, and he may have carried out rudimentary experiments to seek others.

But it was not enough. He had to wait until he discovered the art of glass making before he was able really to add to his power of sight. To do this he had also to increase his knowledge of the properties of light and of how the eye functioned. Only when he combined the knowledge he gained in different fields did he place himself within reach of his now amazing power of "seeing near and seeing far."

During the Paleolithic, or old stone, age, Man discovered how to make fire. He could by then also talk, and he had the beginnings of religion. During the Neolithic, or new stone, age, he became farmer, potter, and weaver. During the bronze age, he became architect, metalworker, mechanic, and wheelwright. The civilization of cities started, and with it, politics, a word derived from the Greek *polis*: city. Writing, commerce, and all the other activities we know in their present complex forms, developed. Not until the iron age did Man become glass maker. By then he had mastery over wood, stone, and metal, which he needed to fashion the equipment for glass making.

Out of the old river civilizations of the Euphrates, the Tigris, and the Nile, going back 3,000 to 4,000 years before Christ, and more perhaps, sprang ultimately the dazzling culture of the ancient Greeks, which reached its heights some 2,500 years ago. Accordingly, we realize the stupendous extent to which Man has extended his power of vision in a comparatively short space of time.

He is today able with his microscopes to see tiny molecules within the living cell and viruses that pass through the finest of filters. Out of such minute observations he has constructed two new and exciting branches of science: molecular biology and virology. He is today able with his telescopes to scan distant corners of the universe. He can do even better. With still, and moving picture, cameras, he can photograph those same distant corners, dispatching his apparatus in space vehicles across distances that make our imaginations boggle. The new information is changing many conceptions of the universe.

Part One: 2

THE art of seeing near and seeing far, of seeing large and seeing small, had its origins in the earliest days of Man's recorded history. It counts as one of Man's outstanding technological achievements and upon it much of experimental science rests. Is not the classic image of the scientist that of a man with a microscope? But, as we have already said, Man first had to understand the properties of light, the way in which we see, and the nature of materials that would enable him to make a lens through which an object under examination might be viewed larger (*magnified*), or smaller (*diminished*). Thus it could be made to reveal more of itself than the naked eye discerned.

From objects we have recovered and dated, and from information yielded by other sources, we have reason to think that glazing was being done about 4000 B.C. By about 3000

B.C., glass making was a well-recognized, if small, industry. For 1,000 years or so, glassware was more uncommon than common. From about 2000 B.C., our evidence thins and we find it difficult to trace developments in the glass making industry, although it is believed that the manufacture of free-standing glass objects started either in Egypt or in Mesopotamia about 2500 B.C. Glass vessels were made only about 1,000 years later. The Romans improved upon Egyptian methods but we see no spectacular advances until more modern times when scientists called urgently for special kinds of optical and resistant glass.

After the fleets of Anthony and Cleopatra were defeated at the battle of Actium (31 B.C.) by Octavian, the Roman Peace (*Pax Romana*) settled. Egypt was added to the Roman Empire and as a result the number of craftsmen engaged in glass making multiplied and the industry itself spread. According to the Greek geographer Strabo (circa 63 B.C.–A.D. 24), who was a great traveler, glass making started in Rome at about the beginning of our own era. Pliny The Elder (circa A.D. 23–79), author of a NATURAL HISTORY, said that the glass making industry was situated at Cumae in the Campania. Clearly craftsmen were also attracted to the northwestern end of the Adriatic, and in time established the reputation of Venetian glass, which we still talk about with such respect and admiration.

Within four centuries, the knowledge of glass making had spread through the valleys of two important French waterways: the Rhone and the Saône, as well as the valley of the Rhine. By about A.D. 400, Cologne in the German Rhineland, Belgium, and northern France, had thriving glass industries. In Britain, glass makers had settled near Colchester and Norwich. The trade gained such a strong footing everywhere that waning Roman power and the withdrawal of legions from various parts of the Empire did it no irreparable damage. Italy remained the chief center of glass making, with Belgium not very far behind.

But what is glass?

Glass is inorganic substance which, even after fusing and cooling remains the same, though cooling does harden it, whereupon it becomes transparent, and sometimes opaque or misty. Glass consists of silicates of lime, soda, and potash, to which are added metallic oxides to give color and opacity, as well as borates and phosphates added for other reasons. Glass makers of the ancient world generally used a mixture of sodium and calcium silicate. The Egyptians, for example, used powdered quartz, steatite (soapstone), and clay, which they stirred together and then fired.

Mixing is the first of three main procedures in glass making and it is known as *fritting*. The mixture itself is known as *frit*, and the frit is fired in the oven. *Firing* is thus the second of the three procedures. Egyptian glass was inclined to be opaque because Egyptian glass makers could not raise sufficiently the temperature of their ovens. But so long as the original materials are clear, the glass itself turns clear. The best safeguard against spoiling is *slow-cooling*. Slow-cooling, the third procedure, known as *annealing*, ensures both tempering and toughening of the hot liquid mass which emerges from the ovens. Indeed, slow-cooling often takes place in a special kind of oven.

Objects made of glass have to be molded from the hot

liquid mass before cooling starts, or they have to be blown, or they have to be ground once the molten substance has cooled and hardened, a process known as *grinding*, or *cold-cutting*. In the ancient world glassware was, for the most part, shaped in clay molds or fashioned around a cone of sand tied up in a cloth bag. The art of glass blowing was probably discovered in Syria during the first century B.C. Until about the middle of the nineteenth century the techniques of glass making remained almost unchanged but, while keeping to main principles, they are nowadays more complicated.

The glass industry became of true value to science only after glass makers learned how to produce lenses, and it is the vital art of lens grinding that over the centuries has provided science with important tools of the trade. The lens began as a simple magnifying and diminishing glass. The Egyptians already realized that a glass ball cut in half can act as a magnifier. They may have realized also that a hollow glass sphere filled with water can magnify. Certainly the Greeks and Romans knew it, as we gather from their writings.

Claudius Ptolemaius (Ptolemy), the Egyptian astronomer of Alexandria (second century A.D.), who assumed the earth was at the center of a fixed planetary system, in his (?) *Optics* (*Perspectiva*), described magnifying glasses and tried to explain how they worked. Doubts exist about his authorship of *Optics*, a valuable book, which was first translated into Arabic, and from Arabic into Latin, probably in the middle of the twelfth century. Many scholars believe that Euclid (third century B.C.) and not Ptolemy wrote the work.

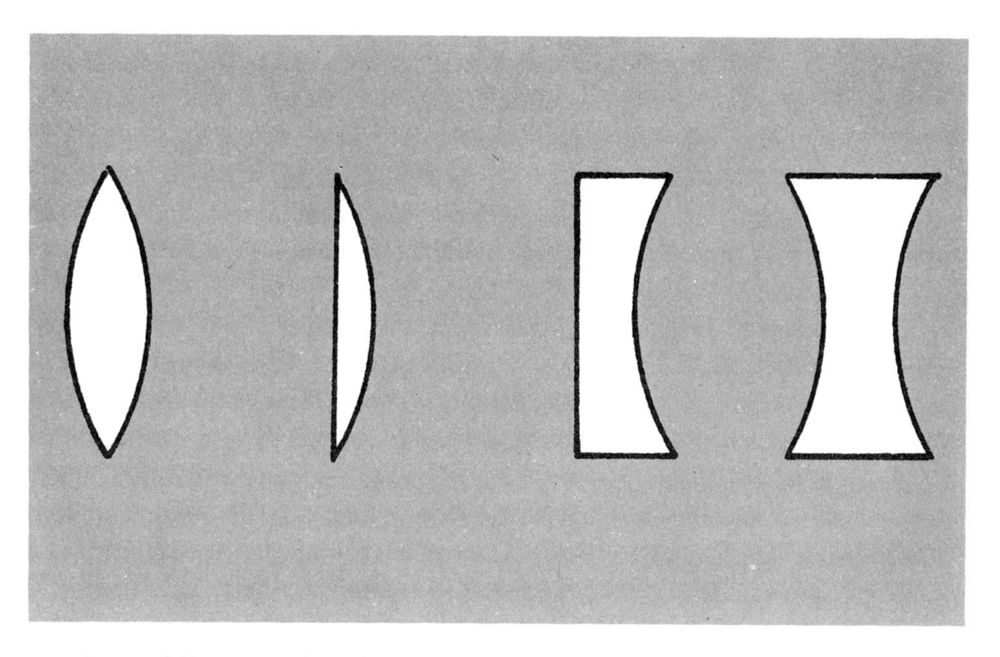

Lenses fall into two broad types: *convergent* and *divergent.* Convergent lenses are best imagined as deriving from two prisms set base to base. Divergent lenses are best imagined as deriving from two prisms set point to point.

We see here (a) biconvex, (b) plano-convex, (c) plano-concave, and (d) biconcave.

Some believe Euclid wrote not only *Optics,* but *Catoptrics* (*Specularia*), another work dealing with optical problems. Still others believe Hero of Alexandria (second century A.D.) to have been the author of *Catoptrics.* Both Euclid and Hero, like Ptolemy, lived in Alexandria, and both were mathematicians. Few of us have not studied Euclid's geometry.

Euclid's *Optics* (if in fact he was the author) consists of six *suppositions*, or statements of basic matters that he believed we could take for granted. Sixty theorems follow, derived from the suppositions. He thought visual "rays" give us our power of sight, and he paid a great deal of attention to the relation between eye and object. How does an object appear to the eye when placed in different positions? He suggested that no visible object is ever seen in its entirety at one and the same time because there are "spaces" between the visual "rays."

Problems of reflection and refraction also fascinated scholars of the ancient world. Indeed, they must from the very start have fascinated Man when he caught sight of his face mirrored in a pool of water or saw a stick in a river or lake that he was deceived into regarding as "bent."

The "bend," we now know, is caused by refraction which takes place because light is deflected at a certain angle when it obliquely enters one medium (in this case, water) from another (in this case, air) of different density.

The author of *Catoptrics* tried to set down a Law of Reflection and to apply it to plane, concave, and convex mirrors, which had also attracted the attention of scholars. Archimedes of Syracuse (287–212 B.C.), a Greek mathematician and inventor, wrote at length on mirrors and asked himself also, *How do people see*? The author of *Catoptrics* guessed that an emission from the eyes gives us the power of sight. Like others before him, he had noted refraction but could offer no satisfactory explanation of it. However, Ptolemy, in *Perspectiva,* tried to verify the Law of Refraction by means of experiment. He employed a measuring instrument, called a *planca,* to which he could conveniently attach a mirror, plane, convex, or concave.

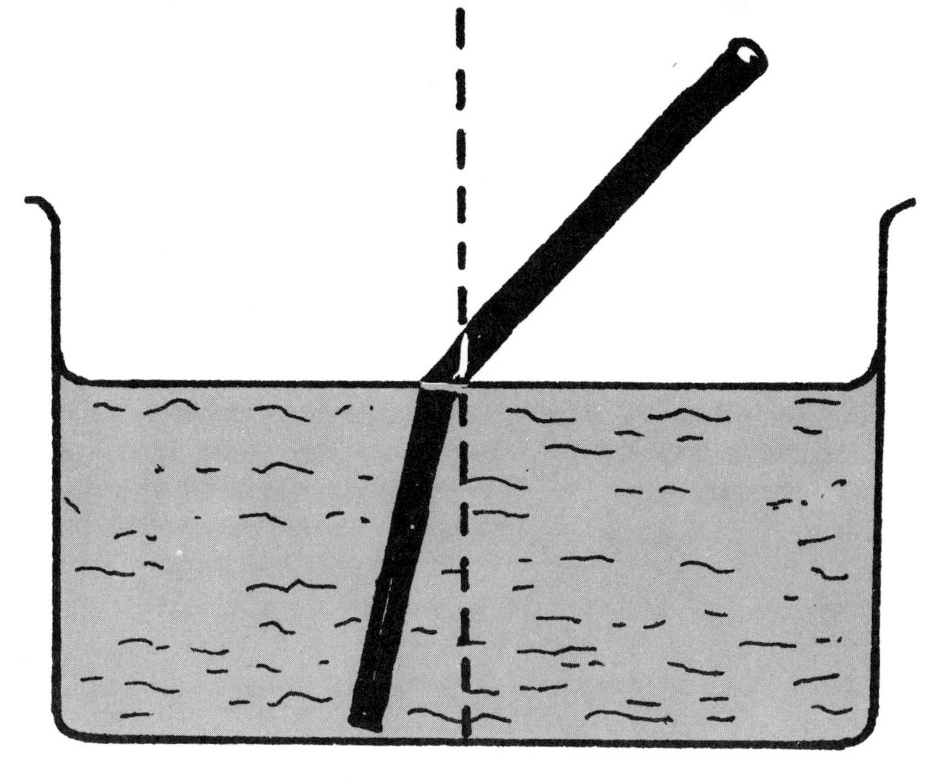

"Bent" stick in water

When a ray is incident in a rarer medium, incident light is refracted always toward the normal by the denser medium.

When a ray is incident in a denser medium, it is refracted always away away from the normal by the rarer medium. Air is a good example of a rarer medium, water of a denser. The "bent" effect of a stick in water is thus caused by refraction.

In his experiments, he followed the path of a visual "ray" from the eye in one medium to an object in another medium and realized that the angle of refraction in some way varies with the angle of incidence, that is, the angle that the path of the ray makes with the perpendicular to the surface at its point of incidence or contact. For his observations, he used a special form of planca made up of a brass circle marked with two diameters at right angles to each other. Each quarter was divided into 90 degrees. Since he was able to place a small colored pin perpendicular to the plane of the circle in one of the upper arcs, and another in the arc of the lower and opposite quarter, he was in a position to measure the angle of incidence, and of refraction, from air to water, air to glass, and water to glass. The table of angles which Ptolemy compiled turned out to be surprisingly accurate, although he failed to hit upon the critical angle. His table is our oldest example, outside the field of astronomy, of measurement in scientific experiment.

Ptolemy also investigated the power of sight and his conclusions on that subject not only form the most interesting portion of his work, but remain the only contribution to dioptrics that has survived from the distant past. (*Dioptrics,* from the Greek *dioptrikos*: an optical instrument. Dioptrics is, therefore concerned with ways of assisting sight, for example, by means of lenses.)

Part One: 3

THE Romans, although they had a flourishing glass industry, appear to have written little about optics. They contributed almost nothing to the advancement of a subject already so well dealt with by the Greeks. When the Roman Empire broke up in the fifth century A.D. the learning of the ancients was for many centuries lost. It trickled back into Western Europe by way of the Arab world, which included Egypt, North Africa, and a large part of Spain. The most important work on optics after that of Ptolemy was written during the tenth century A.D. by Althazen, an Arab scholar born at Basra A.D. 926. He died at Cairo A.D. 1035. Althazen's *Thesaurus of Optics* (*thesaurus* derives from the Greek *thesauros*: treasure, and in this sense means encyclopedia), remained popular until well into the sixteenth century.

Althazen begins with an inquiry into the workings of the

eye. Never before had such an inquiry been carried out in detail. His descriptions show that he had an excellent grasp of how we see. Yet he never gave the wholly correct answer to this highly complex problem. Indeed, some seven centuries had to pass before the secret of vision was penetrated by the German astronomer Johann Kepler (1571–1630), who demonstrated that we could see because the crystalline lens of the eye focuses images upon the retina, a layer at the back of the eyeball, which is highly sensitive to light.

Althazen studied carefully how we see with two eyes (binocular vision). He thought that an image was registered independently by each eye but became a single image in the optic nerve. He built mirrors of various kinds to demonstrate that the angles of incidence and of reflection were the same. He spent much time working out what happened in refraction. He was a careful, accurate observer and he took great pains to build instruments for the verification of his observations. He constructed a planca like Ptolemy's but pressed his investigations further than Ptolemy had done. He does not appear to have followed Ptolemy's example of compiling tables. At any rate, if he did, they have not come down to us.

Scholars of the ancient world seem to have known little or nothing about lenses. In 1270, a Thuringian Pole named Vitello issued a work on optics that was in large part an unacknowledged crib of Athazen's *Thesaurus*, but he had no comment to offer about lenses, which, if they were conceived of in theory, were not manufactured until after 1270. Some authorities have contested this dating, and have suggested that certain articles in the British Museum and elsewhere might be primitive lenses. In the Assyrian Gallery of the British Museum is the Nineveh or Assyrian lens (circa 725 B.C.), while in the Egyptian Gallery are three objects that look as though they might be plano-convex lenses. The Museum of University College, London, contains two similar exhibits. Experts disagree about their identity and their uses but the majority agree that these articles were not designed to magnify or to help vision in any way. They think the articles are ornaments in which the glass is meant simply to glitter attractively. The most telling argument against the existence in ancient times of lenses is that archeologists have never yet unearthed the tools required to manufacture them.

Our first good evidence of the existence of lenses dates from early in the thirteenth century, which leads us reasonably to suppose that scientists had for some time been aware of the usefulness of lenses and had been investigating the possibilities of manufacturing them. Indeed, Robert Grosseteste, Bishop of Lincoln (circa 1175–1253), outlined a theory of optics and stated that lenses could make distant, or small, objects larger.

The appearance of the first lenses coincided with a revival of European learning that was gathering pace during the early part of the thirteenth century. Universities were founded at Paris, Oxford, Bologna, and Salerno, and the students educated there read ardently the works of the Greek philosopher Aristotle (384–322 B.C.), which had reached the hands of European scholars from Arab sources. Aristotle's ideas though often distorted by mistranslation, hit their minds with tremendous force, particularly his inquiries into biology, astronomy, physics, and meteorology. His view of science defied reconciliation with the mythical or abstract explanations of the universe, of our earth, and of Man's presence upon it, which the medieval church insisted were the correct ones. The experimental method in its simpler forms stemmed from the anxiety of students to test some of Aristotle's theories. The English Franciscan, Roger Bacon (1214–94), and the German Dominican, Albert the Great (Albertus Magnus: 1193 or 1206–80), were two whose writings show them in quest of exact knowledge.

Roger Bacon's life remains rather obscure. We know that he had money enough to buy books and instruments with which to further his researches. He taught both at Paris and at Oxford and made a reputation for himself as an instructor. Later he showed up the corruptions of the Church and fell foul of the religious authorities for expressing ideas that ran contrary to theirs. He wrote three works (*Opus Magnus, Opus Minus,* and *Opus Tertium*), that he composed for Pope Clement IV. We are not sure whether Clement ever received them or whether, having received them, he ever read them.

Bacon devoted about a fifth of his writings to optics. The prospect of constructing a concave burning mirror seems to have enthralled him. Indeed, he had a passion for burning glasses, and he made them by filling glass spheres with water, through which he tried to focus the sun's rays on various objects. He tried also to reconcile the views of Ptolemy and Euclid with those of Althazen. Both Ptolemy and Euclid believed that our eyes sent out "rays" which gave us our power of vision. On the other hand Althazen taught that "rays" traveled from the things we wished to see to the eyes. Bacon compromised and maintained that "rays" traveled from the eye *and* from the thing the eye was trying to discern, at one and the same time. The outgoing and incoming rays merged without conflict because, according to Bacon, they were "different" and in no way opposed to each other. Some of his admirers claim that he knew about lenses and compound optical instruments, and that if he did not invent spectacles, at least he suggested them.

The inventor of spectacles resembling even faintly the eyeglasses with which we are now familiar is not readily indentifiable. There is also dispute about the time when spectacles were invented. To begin with, monks poring over their manuscripts appear to have helped their failing eyesight by the use of ordinary magnifying lenses that they held in position with the hand. The inconvenience must have been considerable since it left them only one free hand for whatever work they had to do. Yet this was better than nothing.

Several references to spectacles were made during the early years of the fourteenth century. In 1305, Bernard Gordon, a doctor of Montpellier, France, mentioned spectacles that enabled the elderly to read small letters. In 1306, Friar Giordano of Pisa talked about spectacles during the course of a sermon he gave at Florence, claiming he had actually discussed them with their inventor. Did he mean Brother Alexander of Spina, "a modest and good man" who was reputed to hold the secrets of spectacle making? In the library of the friars of St. Catherine at Pisa is a Latin chronicle containing this piece of information about Brother Alexander. Was, then, Brother Alexander the true inventor of spectacles? Or had he learned about them from somebody else? An inscription in the church of Santa Maria Maggiore in Florence reads: *Here lies Salvino degli Armati of Flor-*

ence, inventor of spectacles. May God pardon his sins. MCCXVVII. The invention of spectacles surely cannot count among his sins for if he really invented them he confered upon his fellow-men an inestimable boon. His spectacles were probably fitted with convex lenses that magnified and were therefore valuable to the elderly with weakening sight.

The most plausible account of the invention of spectacles informs us that while Armati actually devised them, Spina published the secret (circa 1300) in connection with the introduction of a spherical tool which fitted the surface of the lens and enabled an operator to work it into the desired shape.

Spectacles were manufactured, and improved upon in Venice for the Venetian glass industry was expanding in response to public demand for fine ware and for window glass. The by-laws of the Venetian Guilds refer to "little discs for the eyes," and, in 1301, refer more precisely to "eye-glasses for reading." By 1316, we hear of spectacles for sale at six *soldi Bolognese*, *soldo*, plural *soldi*, being the Italian halfpenny. Thirty-six years later (1352) Tomasso Barasino of Modena painted the first portrait we have of a man wearing spectacles.

For some time convex magnifying lenses were probably the only kind in use. Not until the fifteenth century do we find mention of concave lenses. Nicholas, Cardinal of Cusa (1401–64), reports in a book that the beryl is a resplendent, colorless, and transparent stone to which is given convex or concave form. Those who look through it, he adds, succeed in discovering things at first invisible. At the end of the fourteenth century, the beryl and rock crystal were often regarded as the only materials that could safely be used for making "reading-stones" or eyeglasses. Since glass was by no means plentiful, the optical instruments of those days were very costly. In 1300, shortage forced the Superintendent of the Arts at Venice to forbid the use of glass for aids to eyesight and only in the year following was his ban relaxed.

Thus the theoretical studies of Euclid, Ptolemy, Althazen, Vitello, and others bore fruit. What is of special importance is that the invention of spectacles led to the invention of the microscope.

Part One: 4

WE HAVE told already the tall story about the system of mirrors Caesar erected to spy on Britons. Yet another tall story concerns a magic mirror, on top of the lighthouse at Alexandria in Egypt, which was believed capable of revealing objects 500 leagues away. From such exaggerations to primitive spectacles that consisted of two glasses suspended by two pieces of leather, themselves fastened to a cap drawn over the forehead, may strike us as a step down. But always the important thing is escape from overblown fantasy to the beginnings, however modest, of reality. Not until the fifteenth century did glasses start looking more like those we today see resting on the bridge of the nose. Although the Venetians of the sixteenth century were making adequate lenses, although the *camera obscura* (a device for projecting the images of distant objects so that they can be traced out on paper or other surface), had been invented, and although rudimentary compound optical instruments had been manufactured, the mathematical basis of optics remained somewhat immature. Optics as a science did not advance notably until its theoretical foundations were more securely laid.

The Renaissance was a period when artists greatly stimulated science by abandoning ideal forms and traditional symbols, and by trying to see life as it really was. They started to observe Nature in detailed manner and to introduce rocks, mountains, birds, beasts, and other natural features into their pictures. Slowly they gained mastery of perspective, which Filippo Brunelleschi (1377–1446), the first of the great Renaissance architects, had pioneered.

The link between optics as a science and the arts was well forged by Leon Battista Alberto (1404–72) in a treatise (*Trattato della Pittura*) he wrote in 1434. The son of a wealthy Florentine family that had been banished for political reason, he searched out knowledge among people of all classes. He urged the use of perspective and thought that to represent three-dimensional figures in two dimensions was the artist's primary objective. Painters, he declared, ought to know their geometry, and they ought to employ such devices as the rectangular-coordinates net for plotting the field of vision, and the *camera obscura* for landscapes. Leonardo da Vinci (1452–1519), with his deep scientific preoccupation, echoed Alberti's strongly held views. He asserted that the science of painting (note the word *science*) dealt among other things with the relative nearness and distance of bodies, and with the degree of diminution required as distances gradually increase. Moreover, he asserted, this science is the mother of perspective, that is, of the science of visual "rays."

The inventor of the *camera obscura,* like the inventor of spectacles, cannot easily be determined. Indeed, the history of the *camera obscura* is confused. Did Brunelleschi use it, or something like it, to make drawings? Alberti advocated its employment in his treatise of 1434. On the other hand, the principles underlying its construction were mentioned by Francesco Maurolico (1494–1575), whose family was driven out of Constantinople by the Turkish invasion of 1453 and settled first at Messina in Italy, and then at Naples. Yet Maurolico does not admit to having made one. Girolamo Cardan (1507–76) also dealt with the possibilities of the *camera obscura* without ever being wholly clear about the subject. In 1569, Daniello Barbaro, a nobleman of Venice, referred, as had de Cusa, to concave spectacles for the construction of a "camera" to aid drawing by projection, the *camera obscura* in fact. "Take an old Man's glass, convex on both sides," he wrote, "not concave like the glasses of youths of short sight." Barbaro's account indicates how very much the *camera obscura* was "in the air."

The real puzzle, therefore, is that many scholars credit Giambattista Della Porta of Naples (1536–1603) with the invention of the *camera obscura* because in his book *Natural Magick* (1589), which was not translated into English until 1658, he set out the principles governing the construction not only of the *camera obscura,* but of the kaleidoscope and a whole range of curious glasses. Della Porta is favored as the inventor because he instructs his readers how to make a *camera obscura;* yet it is hard to reconcile this claim with Alberti's reference to such a piece of equipment some 185 years earlier.

Interest in constructing optical instruments was accompanied by continuing interest in how the eyes function. Maurolico showed that light fell on the lens of the eye, to be focused in turn upon the retina; and by 1600, Geronimo Fabrizio (1537–1619) showed that the lens of the eye was in front, rather than in the middle where it had traditionally been sited. Della Porta, in 1593, published at Naples a truly scientific study, not a popularization, of optics, in which he examined refraction of light, the human eye, and the processes of vision, and he also speculated about why stars twinkle. He believed the twinkling effect was due to vapors in the atmosphere that caused rays of light to be dissipated. He thought our ability to see distant objects could be improved by combining in some way concave and convex lenses, an idea that had been anticipated by Fracastorius of Verona (d. 1555) who stated that if anybody looked through two spectacle glasses, one superimposed upon the other, he would see everything nearer and greater, even the stars.

Was he hinting at the possibility of an invention such as the telescope? Certainly the idea of bringing distant objects into closer view was occupying the minds of scientists everywhere. In England, John Dee (1527–1608), a geographer, known also as an astrologer, who improved upon the methods of drawing up navigational charts, and Leonard Digges (1510–55), who first measured parallaxes, both experimented with this end in view. Digges's was a most useful feat since parallax, which must be allowed for, presents astronomers with a constantly vexing problem. But what is parallax? It is the apparent displacement of an object caused by actual change of the point from which it is observed. The significance of the definition becomes instantly plainer when we remember that the Earth is, so to speak, a moving platform from which we try to make observations of other moving bodies.

Meanwhile, writing about spectacles, Della Porta said: "If using convex glasses an object be placed near the glass and if the eye be placed either near or far, the object will be seen erect." He also said that old men would see more clearly with convex spectacles. Did he devise a telescope of sorts? Some historians of science believe he might have because he stated that a combination of convex lenses should overcome distance and draw objects nearer to the eye.

In truth, the inventor of the telescope is as hard to select as the inventor of the *camera obscura* or the inventor of spectacles. For some time people had been hearing of "Holland glass," a primitive form of telescope, which, evidently devised in Holland, could also be purchased in Brussels and in Paris. Dutch opticians like Metius (Jakob Andrianzoon of Alkmaar), Lippershey, and Jansen were making and selling "Holland glass" around the year 1608.

"Holland glass" appears to have been at first regarded as an amusing plaything, and the story goes that a child set off the manufacture of telescopes. Gazing through one lens at another in the window of Jan Lippershey's shop in 1600, this child noticed that objects were drawn much closer. A delighted announcement to this effect set Lippershey thinking, and so telescopes came into being. Some authorities believe the telescope to have been invented as a result of chance observations by Johannes Jansen, a Dutch spectacle maker who had the perception to combine a convex objective and a concave eye lens in order to secure an erect image. Certainly his son, Zacharias, claimed that his father had, in 1604, made the first telescope. He confessed at the same time that his father had followed an Italian model of 1590. Was this model the creation of Della Porta? Was it a real instrument, the product of an Italian workshop? Or was it no more than drawings and plans that the elder Jansen had managed to get hold of? We cannot answer these baffling questions.

There is some evidence for awarding the palm to Jansen who figures as the originator of both telescope and microscope, even if the distinction between the two was not absolutely clear in those times. A telescope, when looked into at the "wrong" end, or "upside down," could serve as a microscope with an extremely limited field of vision. William Boreel, a Dutch envoy in England, wrote: "Middleburg, the capital of Zeeland, is my home. . . . In 1561, when I was born, Hans Jansen inhabited a neighboring house. I knew his son, Zacharias, and was as a boy often in his shop. This Hans, and his son, Zacharias, as I often heard, first invented the microscope." Boreel declared that a fellow-Dutchman, Cornelius Drebbel (1572–1634), who taught James I mathematics, once showed him a microscope that had in all probability been brought over from Zeeland in 1604. "The instrument," he noted, "has a gilt brass tube 1½ feet long and 2 inches in diameter and is supported on three brass dolphins." There is no reason for us to discount the story for Drebbel was a remarkable man of science who built a submarine, which he displayed on the Thames. He also made a fortune by introducing a red dye.

A serious counter-claimant to Jansen was established when an application for a patent by Metius came to light among the papers of his countryman, Christian Huygens, of whom we shall soon have a great deal to say. Moreover, the document is supported by a statement made independently by the French scholar René Descartes, who lived in Holland, and of whom we shall also have more to say. According to Descartes: ". . . Metius, an unlearned man, but one who loved to make mirrors and burning glasses, having by him glasses of various shapes, thought of looking through two of them, one convex and one concave; and luckily he put them in the end of a tube, and thus the first telescopes were made."

It is, perhaps, a little disappointing for us not to be able to credit the invention of the telescope and microscope to some scientific genius, and to have to admit that they were by-products of the spectacle making industry. The need for them had long existed and there seems little reason for the delay in their arrival. By the sixteenth century the optical industry was really flourishing and required new outlets for both its energy and its resources. Telescopes and microscopes were, first and foremost, novelties that their manufacturers hoped might intrigue people, sell in quantity, and bring satisfactory profits.

Part One: 5

THE theory that the universe was static and that our earth was at its center had been sacred from the time of Ptolemy who had in fact "borrowed" it from Hipparchus, a Greek astronomer of the second century B.C. After about 1,500 years the Polish astronomer Nicolaus Copernicus (1473–1543) questioned it. He hypothesized a dynamic universe with the earth rotating about its own axis and moving with other planets round a fixed sun. The idea was not entirely new since Aristarchus of Samos (310–230 B.C.) had almost had to pay with his life for putting it forward in his own time.

Copernicus was convinced that if other planets and stars moved, the earth also moved. He proved his supposition by using a quadrant, an armillary sphere, and a triquetrum which enabled him to judge the height above the horizon of

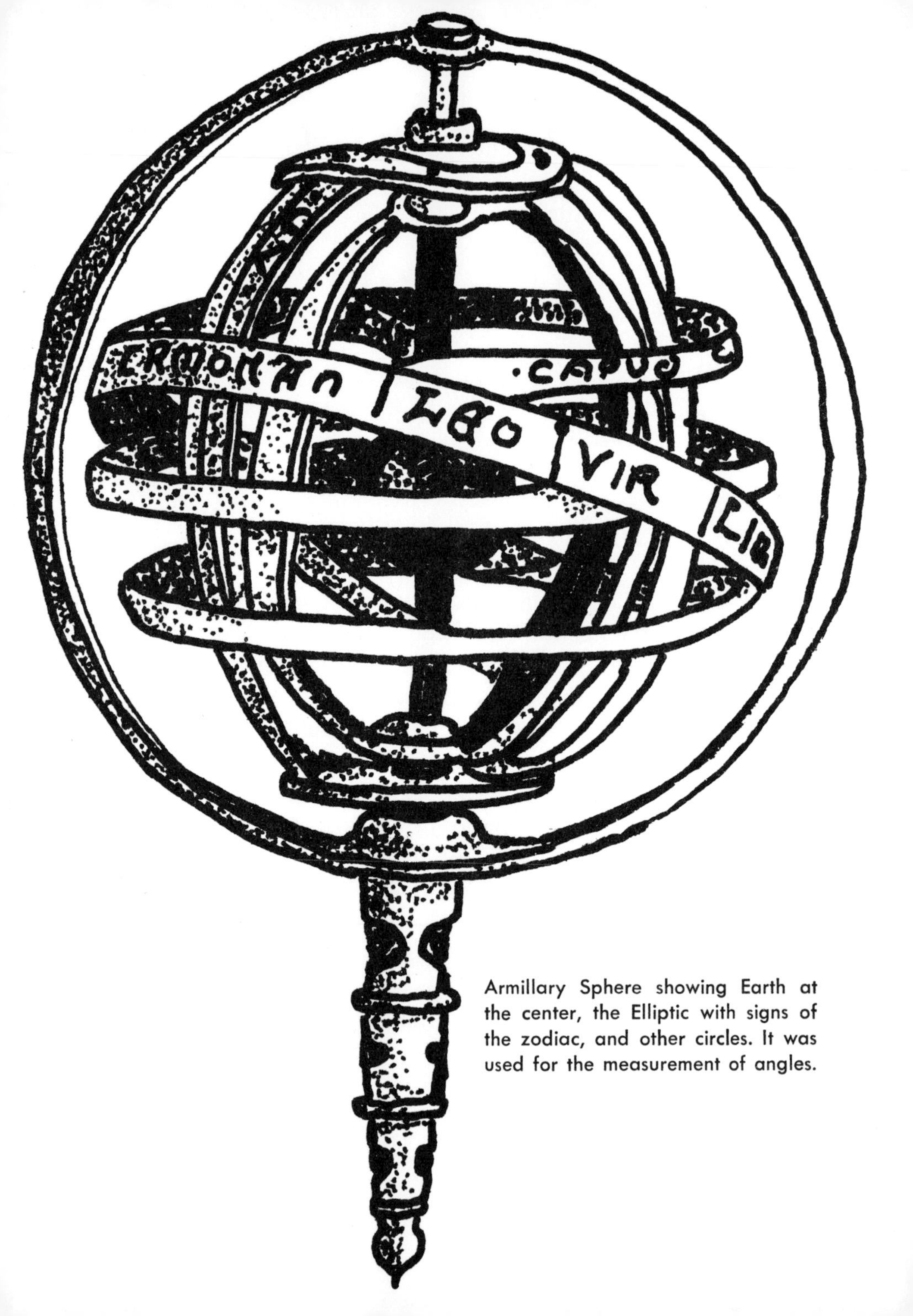

Armillary Sphere showing Earth at the center, the Elliptic with signs of the zodiac, and other circles. It was used for the measurement of angles.

celestial bodies. His equipment was simple, even crude, but it was enough.

Nevertheless, he waited until 1543, some thirty-six years, before publishing his views in his book *De Revolutionibus Orbium Celestium* (*On the Revolution of Celestial Orbs*). Indeed, he actually lay dying as he examined the first copy. Why did he delay?

Copernicus was a canon of the cathedral at Frauenberg, and although he hardly spent his life in pious works, he was too timid to challenge the authority of the Church which held Ptolemy's ideas to be true. Had he made a challenge he would almost certainly have been summoned to answer to the Inquisition, so we cannot be too severe on him for evading such a daunting fate.

Although the Copernican picture of the universe with a rotating earth moving with other planets round the sun was a purely astronomical one, he presented it not as science but as philosophy, according to the custom of the day.

The Italian mathematician and astronomer, Galileo Galilei (1564–1642) was also convinced that the Copernican view was the correct one, and he became immediately absorbed by the revolution in science that he knew had to follow acceptance of it. He faced many troublesome questions. For example: How could the earth go around without causing an enormous wind? And if it did go around and around, how was it that a shot from a cannon was not deflected?

Most of us have heard the story of how Galileo dropped two stones of unequal weight from the top of the Leaning

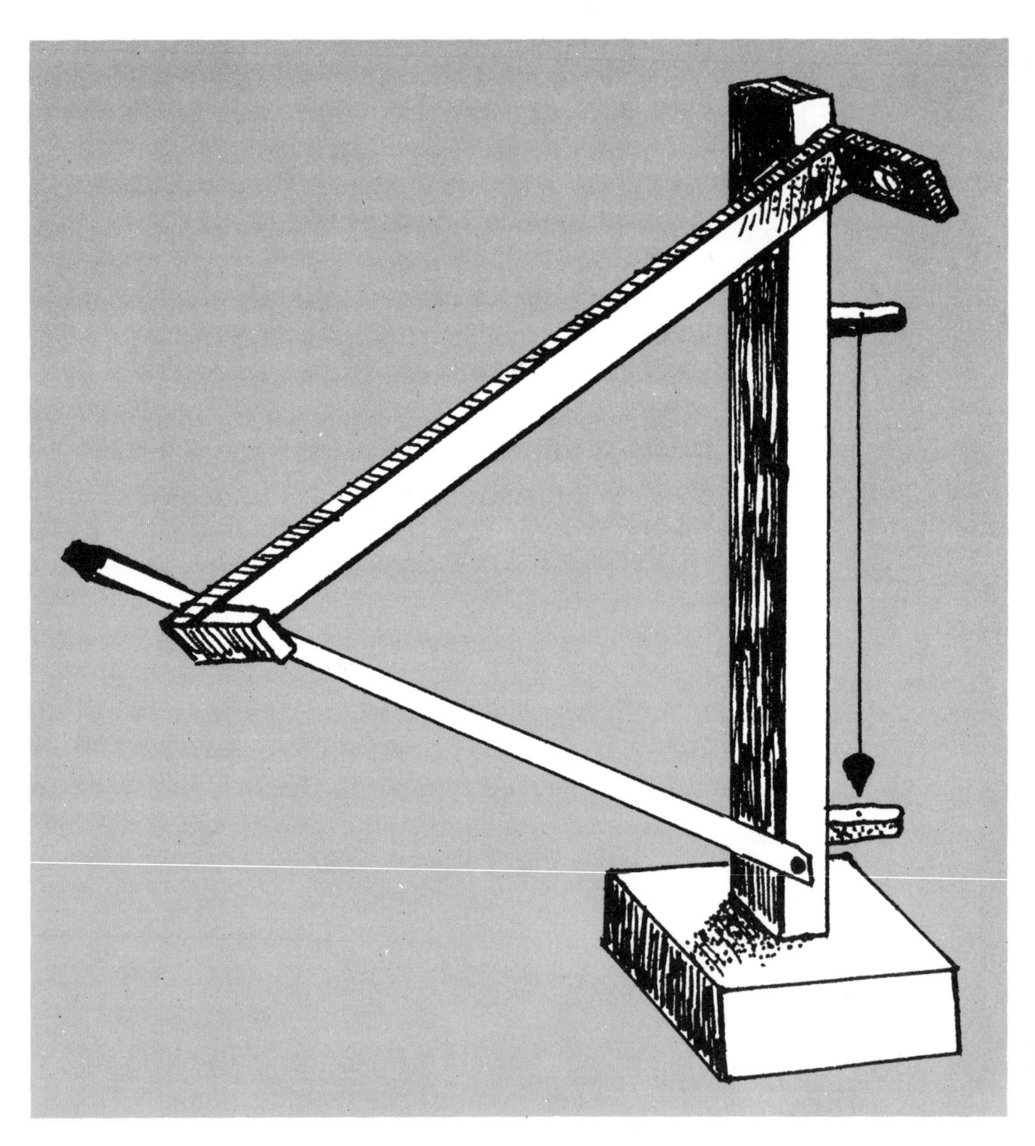

Triquetrum or Ptolemy's Ruler

Tower at Pisa in order to show that both fell to earth at one and the same time. The famous story may or may not be true, but he became deeply absorbed in such matters as the swing of pendulums and the conduct of bodies in free motion.

Galileo carried out some of the first real experiments in European science, and he offered one of its most substantial maxims: *Measure that which can be measured. Make measurable that which cannot yet be measured.* He combined exact experiment with mathematical analysis, a method followed ever since with resounding success by generations of scientists. He also linked mechanics and mathematics. He was, nevertheless, a theoretical scientist, first and foremost, who achieved wonderful feats of imagination. He could hardly have been other in an age when experimental science, of which he was a pioneer, was just coming into being.

It is an odd feature of the odd history of telescope and microscope that Galileo seems not to have heard of the Italian instrument to which the younger Jansen referred. In 1609, he got news from a correspondent in Paris that a Dutch telescope existed. Immediately he set about trying to arrange concave and convex lenses in various combinations until they gave him the sort of results Dutch opticians were reported to have obtained. Finally he constructed a telescope to his satisfaction and began to observe the heavens through it. It was with this primitive piece of equipment that he accomplished deeds in astronomy which we still regard with amazement. He turned the simple telescope into the outstanding scientific instrument of his own, and of other, days.

He has justifiably been named the proper originator of the astronomical telescope.

Two of Galileo's instruments are still on exhibition at the Physics Museum in Florence. They strike us as absurdly unambitious, consisting simply of tubes with convex lenses at one end and concave lenses for the eye pieces. They magnified some 20 times. Yet these unambitious instruments revealed to Galileo a whole new world outside our own, whose nature, as he perceived it, enabled him to set forth a fresh picture of the universe.

The spring evenings of April, 1609, gave him clear opportunity because the skies were clear. His most powerful telescope had a 2¼-inch objective and magnified some 30 times. The moon, far from being smooth and serene, displayed itself to him as very like our own Earth. It had mountains and valleys, and he watched the shadows on it grow longer as the sun gradually set. Aristotle, approaching nature as a philosopher rather than as a practical astronomer, decreed that heavenly bodies had to be perfectly round. Any other shape would be unfitting to their dignity, so they had to be conceived of as spheres, as perfect orbs. Aristotle had decreed also that the sun's integrity could never be assailed — its perfection was eternal.

Yet Galileo saw spots and other agitations upon the sun's surface. He observed that not only the moon, but the planet Venus also showed phases, that is, varying stages of change, especially in the degree of illumination. How could Venus shows phases if it did not circle the sun as the moon circles the earth? The planet Saturn seemed to him as though it were divided in three. ("I found it threefold.") There can be no doubt he had perceived dimly through his simple telescope the rings of Saturn which he would have discerned clearly with a more efficient piece of equipment.

But the most intriguing revelation of the heavens was, perhaps, that he spotted three stars, then a fourth, circling the planet Jupiter. He had in fact caught sight of four of Jupiter's moons or satellites: Io, Europa, Ganymede, and Callisto. And so there before his eyes, was a Copernican universe in miniature; it was visible to anybody who cared to pick up a telescope and look. A disciple of Copernicus and his Theory of the Universe, Galileo was filled with pleasure to have the truth of it demonstrated, not as philosophy but as science. He went on to gather in a richer catch. He counted in the Pleiades some forty stars where previously only six had been presumed to exist. In Orion's Belt and Sword he added up eighty where previously only seven had been presumed to exist. There were stars, stars everywhere. The Milky Way itself was a shimmer of stars.

But Galileo had to do more than hand over his telescope to the inquiring and invite them to see for themselves so that they might reverse the belief of centuries according to the evidence of their own eyes. He had to prove to them in a manner none could gainsay that the sun was at the center of our universe and that the rotating earth moved around the sun, together with the other planets. He had to explain, also, why the earth's rotation did not cause an enormous wind or deflect shots from a cannon. On the other hand to make such pronouncements was risky. The Dutchman Johann Fabricius (1587–1615) peering through his "Holland glass" had noted sunspots. So had Christopher Scheiner (1575–1650). But neither had spoken out of fear of the consequences. Scheiner, a German Jesuit priest, had thought about it and consulted his superiors only to dismiss it instantly from his mind. Not until 1626, did he start publishing in *Rosa Ursina* his views about sunspot areas and other such problems.

Part One: 6

WITHIN 1½ years of making his first telescope, Galileo published (in 1610) his own *Siderius Nuncius* (*Messenger from the Stars*), in which he set out his discoveries. It created as great a sensation as Charles Darwin's *Origin of Species* was to create when it came out in 1859. The Medici family, and Rome, showered their congratulations upon Galileo. Pisa University invited him to become a professor there. The telescope grew into something of a craze and everybody who could afford to lay hands on an instrument did so in order to survey the marvels of the heavens.

At the hub of the scientific revolution was Galileo. But what was its central issue? From his earliest days, Man had built up a picture of the world around him that was "ideal," drawn from what he imagined things to be rather than what they really are. He invented causes where events defeated his understanding, preferring supernatural to natural explanations because he is an inveterate mystery-maker. The play of imagination which yielded myth has seemed always more attractive than plain reality, often harsh and awesome. Since the time of Galileo science has been picking remorselessly at Man's cherished imaginative conception of himself and of the world in which he lives, moves, and has his being. And how utterly different is the reality it has disclosed!

Not unexpectedly a veritable crop of star discoveries followed Galileo's original enterprise. Simon Mayer, in 1612, spotted a cloudy light in the skies near Andromeda. He said it was "like a candle seen at night through a sheet of horn." He had detected the great nebula of Andromeda, a galaxy like our own. Two years before, Nicolas Fabri de Peiresc, of Aix, France, had noticed the same sort of cloudy light near Orion, which was in fact the nebula of Orion. Then in 1620, a Belgian, Charles Malapert, detected the phases of Mercury. If both Venus and Mercury showed phases there could be few doubts left about the authenticity of the Copernican hypothesis to which Galileo pinned his faith.

Curiously enough the true message of the heliocentric universe (from the Greek *helios*: sun, meaning centered around the sun) which now opposed the old conception of the geocentric universe (from the Greek *gē*: earth, meaning centered around the earth) took some time to penetrate the mind of authority. It was twenty-four years after the publication of *Messenger of the Stars* that Galileo was brought before the Holy Office in Rome and condemned for proclaiming in his *Dialogues of the Two Great Systems of the*

World, the Ptolemaic and the Copernican (1632), that the earth moved, a heresy he was forced to recant. But there were preliminaries to this drastic finale.

In 1616, the Church, sensing the depth of the challenge to its authority, ordered its experts, or Qualifiers, to pronounce on the thesis that the sun is the center of the world, that the earth is not the center of the world and not immovable but capable of motion in harmony with the whole system of the universe, as well as daily about its own axis. The Qualifiers declared the first of these two ideas to be "foolish and absurd;" the second was described as worthy of censure in philosophy and an error of faith. Galileo was accordingly bidden to stop putting it about that ours was a heliocentric universe with the earth and other planets traveling around the sun.

Dialogues on the Two Great Systems was Galileo's witty and ironic response. He was impatient and combative by nature, and he was bitten with the desire to show that those who condemned the heliocentric theory as foolish and absurd could not themselves have been more foolish or more absurd for having done so. He was perfectly aware that he ran great risks but he protected himself so far as he could by larding his book with statements in praise of the Church. Lulled by Galileo's appeasing overtones the Vatican gave its approval. The Pope figured as one of Galileo's characters, charged with the responsibility of defending Ptolemy's old theory of the geocentric universe, and it dawned at last that under the harmless and respectful surface there lurked an explosive thesis likely to endanger seriously the established position built up on the theories of Aristotle and Ptolemy.

Galileo's trial has been misrepresented as the dreaded ordeal of Europe's greatest scientist at the age of sixty-nine. The Church could hardly be expected to deviate from its own laws, but he was not treated with undue severity. The triumph was nevertheless, Galileo's; he alone gained the day for the Copernican system over the Ptolemaic, even if this may not immediately have been clear to the people of his times. The Church itself held out for some 200 years and not until the nineteenth century did it acknowledge at last that ours is not a geocentric but a heliocentric universe.

Meanwhile scientists themselves were forced into a strange double game. They accepted the Church's ruling as a matter of form but pursued their researches upon the assumption that the sun was at the center of the world. We know, they declared with their tongues firmly in their cheeks, that the earth is the heart of our system. But let us for a moment suppose the sun is the heart, impossible though we know this to be. Through this vein of calculated duplicity they managed to avoid the worst consequences that might have followed the publication of astronomical ideas persistently classified as heresy.

Galileo's scientific revolution stood firmly upon the chance discovery of the telescope in Holland and upon his construction of such an instrument when he heard incidentally from a correspondent in Paris of its existence. The need to understand the motion of falling bodies had led him first to study them in equilibrium and to lay the foundations of the science of statics. Next he studied them in motion and laid the foundation of dynamics. As though the foundation of two new scientific departments were not enough, he took advantage of various developments in mathematics and linked mathematics to mechanics. He not only proposed various Laws of Motion but analyzed the strength of materials by means of mathematics. His attack on the old Ptolemaic viewpoint was thus the crowning point of an extraordinarily fruitful career. And, as though in a last gesture of dismissal to the passing world, he wrote his celebrated *Dialogues on the Two Great Systems* not in Latin, the language of clerics, but in Italian, so that he might be understood by all his countrymen.

Men of Science Conquer New World

Part Two: I

FACED with the chaotic conditions in which they lived, thinkers of the Middle Ages strove to present the picture not only of an ordered world, but of a world order. They looked over their shoulders at the past and longed for the kind of order they imagined had been established and enjoyed by the ancients. During the twelfth century Aristotle's works on physics and biology were recovered for Western Europe; they immediately perturbed philosophers. Aristotle's theme was chiefly nature, and the discovery for ourselves of nature, which seemed opposed to supernature, the word of God vouchsafed to us through the revelations of the Bible. To reconcile such opposites has over the ages been the despair of thinkers, and their reconciliation today seems farther off than ever because the stupendous revelations of science themselves suggest that there can be almost nothing left in heaven to surpass them.

The problem has long continued as a clash between faith and reason. Can the chasm that separates them ever be bridged? The Dominican Thomas Aquinas (1220–74), in his *Summa contra Gentiles,* tried to show that faith and reason were not imcompatible. In 1879, less than 100 years ago, Pope Leo XIII directed that Catholic theology should rest upon Aquinas's solution of this and other equally vexing problems, and the Pope's directive is to this day in force, offering an overwhelming compliment not so much to the intellectual prowess of Aquinas as to the intractability of a problem which defies up-to-date resolution.

Having turned Aristotelian science and religious belief into bedfellows, the Church understandably had no wish to see this union disturbed lest old convulsions recur. Such were the deeper reasons behind the opposition to Galileo, who, nevertheless, proved in the long run irresistible.

The science of Aristotle wilted gradually under the attack which was, strangely enough, especially severe from a priest of Provence, in southern France, Abbé Gassendi (1592–1655), who first watched the passage of Mercury before the sun in 1631, or as we may better put it, the transit of Mercury. Gassendi was not only priest and astronomer but also mathematician and meteorologist. He proposed again an atomic theory which Democritus (circa 460–322 B.C.), a Thracian, had long before advanced, without ever being aware, perhaps, of the far-reaching effects his ideas were to have on science. Democritus imagined the universe to consist of atomic particles moving in a void, in empty space. They were of varying forms and thus they could combine, like the pieces of a jigsaw puzzle, to make the innumerable shapes of everything in the world. Whatever we saw as change, said Democritus, was no more than the movement of atoms. His idea of a void, an emptiness, was an audacious challenge to the views of the orthodox thinkers who asserted their disbelief in the possibility of void or emptiness. To them, the universe was full, a *plenum* (space filled with matter), a word deriving from the Latin *plenus:* full.

Gassendi's atomic theory visualized large particles moving in the vacuum that scientists after Galileo had proved could exist. How could Gassendi, a priest, subscribe to a purely materialistic notion that did not need the conception of God's hand constantly at work to maintain a balance that He had by His Will decreed in advance? Moreover, the Church relied on Plato and Aristotle who attributed to heaven ideal forms which grew less than perfect only because of our own less than perfect vision of them. Gassendi merely said that God's hand need not be operating continuously to sustain the workings of our universe and of all things in it. God had, as it were, given the whole immense system its original send-off. Once it was under way, He did not need to interfere with its workings because at the send-off, which also marked the beginning of time, he had settled its whole future unto eternity. He stood, therefore, like a mechanic-in-chief, to oversee the vast engine which He had set in motion.

What we have to note is the arrival of dynamic views to replace the older, more static, concepts of the universe. Using mathematics as a tool, scientists explored, so far as possible, the whole field of nature's workings. Mathematics enabled them to build up theories to account for at least some of those workings. With this tendency went the desire to substitute for abstractions and ideal pictures a more concrete and proven view of the world. Practical problems, such as how mariners might navigate correctly by the stars, or how they might settle their longitudinal position on a chart, absorbed scholars. They were inclined to accept the heliocentric universe of Copernicus and Galileo but they had not demonstrated how it operated in physical terms. The science of optics, and then the theory of light, had become exceptionally important with the astounding success of the telescope in astronomy and with the successes of the microscope in biology that were to follow in the not very distant future. Thus grew up the very methods and techniques through which the technological revolution of the eighteenth century was able to transform ours into an industrial civilization.

In such circumstances, a variety of scientific instruments was needed, each for doing a specific job. When we compare our own laboratories, full of intricate equipment running on electricity, with those in which scientists of former days made their outstanding discoveries, we experience a sense of humility. They managed to overcome the technical handicaps they faced in ways which were highly original. Even during the nineteenth century, the "Great Age" of science, laboratory equipment was comparatively simple. Of all instruments, the telescope became in due course too expensive and too large to house except in a place specially constructed for its installation. On the other hand, smaller models could be turned out by those with a bent for hobbies, especially in the days before science fell into different departments each manned by its own kind of expert. During the seventeenth century, and indeed until recently. Everyman was often his own scientist, experimenting in kitchen, workroom, attic, and often making surprisingly worthwhile contributions to knowledge. This applied particularly in astronomy where the "amateur" repeatedly covered himself with glory, as we shall increasingly appreciate whenever we touch the lives and works of telescopists.

One great amateur of science, of autocratic temperament, zealously critical mind, and with money enough to transform himself into a professional — if rather a bizarre professional — was Tycho Brahe (1546–1601). Brahe not only helped to gain acceptance of the Copernican theory, but devised those instruments essential to observing and calculating the orbits of the planets. Even Copernicus conceived of planetary orbits as perfectly circular, a notion reverting to the "classical" view that the grandeur of the creation demanded that it should consist of orbs that moved in perfect circles. Tycho Brahe was a strangely complex scientist whose prime virtue was that he never advanced any conclusion in astronomy without proper observations. Yet, like so many men of his time, he had profound faith in astrology!

When Tycho Brahe was a boy he watched a partial eclipse of the sun and was deeply impressed, not only by the phenomenon, but by the way astronomers had been able to forecast it. He wondered whether they were always so accurate and thought there might be a chance of catching them out. To start with he obtained a copy of the Alphonsine Tables which had been prepared by Arab and Jewish astronomers at the behest of King Alfonso X of Castille (1223–84). Already some 300 years old when Tycho Brahe first saw them, they were based on the Ptolemaic system. He obtained also the Prutenic Tables, which the German astronomer Erasmus Rheinhold (1511–53) had compiled in 1551 according to the Copernican system. Both sets of tables gave the position of the planets which Tycho Brahe set out to check. He found himself disagreeing with them. Accordingly he resolved that his foremost task was to plot with the greatest possible accuracy the position of the fixed stars. From fixed points he could calculate the course and movement of the planets. What he needed was instruments far more competent than any he could lay hands upon.

Tycho Brahe was lucky enough to discover a benefactor whose liberality seemed boundless. Frederick II of Denmark gave him the island of Hven, about fourteen miles from Copenhagen, and enough money not only to put up an observatory but to staff and run it. On Hven rose Uraniborg, a red-brick palace in the Renaissance style sprouting sharp turrets which were in fact revolving observation towers. At no great distance southward was Stjerneborg, an observatory built underground to safeguard instruments against wind and weather, its domes alone pushing above ground level. The instruments were for the most part of metal instead of wood; but Tycho Brahe, odd though it may seem, did not have the telescope, simply because it had not yet been introduced as an astronomer's tool of trade.

Tycho Brahe's great dream of producing an almanac more correct than the Alphonsine or Prutenic tables collapsed with the death of his patron, Frederick, in 1588.

Overbearing, tyrannical, exacting the strictest obedience from inferiors and acknowledging no superiors, Tycho was submerged when he was deprived of money and powerful patronage. He was forced out of his kingdom of Hven in 1597 and sought refuge in Bohemia. In a short time the fantastic Uraniborg and Stjerneberg lay ruined, smashed down by the hatred of his enemies, so thoroughly that all traces seemed to have vanished. Not until 1951, were a few remnants of their existence uncovered. The famous instruments all vanished; the peasant girl Tycho Brahe had married died in poverty. Accompanied by one or two faithful assistants, he himself died at Prague four years after being expelled from Hven. But not before he was joined there, in 1600, by Johann Kepler (1571–1630), an absent-minded mathematician, to whom Tycho Brahe with penetrating intuition left his papers, his sole possessions in this world. He had smelled out Kepler's genius.

Tycho had experienced life in despotic splendor, even if he ended with nothing. And he had devoted himself ruthlessly to a grand scientific purpose. Kepler's experiences were entirely contrary. He spent his days teetering on the brink of penury, a sick, almost destitute instructor at the University of Graz in Austria. Born in the southwestern German province of Würtemberg, he had studied theology at Tübingen but found mathematics and astronomy a great deal more rewarding. His professor there, Michael Maestline, was a believer in the heliocentric universe and conveyed to Kepler his belief. In 1596, Kepler not only took up his appointment at Graz, he also published a book of which he sent Tycho Brahe a copy.

Tycho Brahe was instantly attracted. He invited the poor young professor, already the father of five, to come and work with him in Prague. The two men could not have been more different. Tycho Brahe never allowed his mental clarity to be dimmed by vague and mystical ideas when trying to solve the problems of astronomy. He thirsted for instruments whose accuracy could never be questioned. Kepler was on the other hand the slave of an overactive mystical imagination which provoked him to extraordinary fits of religious fervor. He was so ingenuous that he actually stated quite solemnly that God gave stars as a gift to Man so that he should not lose his way by night. Tycho Brahe was often exasperated almost beyond endurance by Kepler's fancies. Yet he refrained from breaking with him because he sensed Kepler's authentic scientific genius.

Kepler, once his patron died, led a rather gypsylike existence, obtaining a livelihood first here and then there, with a dozen children to support. In 1609, he published his *The New Astronomy, Founded on a Study of the Motion of Mars* in which he enunciated the first two of his laws. In 1619, after seventeen years of research, he issued his *Harmony of the World,* containing the third of his laws. We need not here go into these laws, except to say that they changed the face of astronomy by demonstrating that the paths followed by the planets were not perfectly circular, but elliptical. Moreover, by his calculations, the exact dimensions of the planetary orbits were established. Where before the picture of our universe was often indecisive, Kepler turned it into one that was not only decisive, but strictly predictable by means of mathematics.

In 1627, he was ready with the tables on which Tycho Brahe had set his heart. From records Tycho entrusted to him, Kepler produced an up-to-date almanac based not on his old patron's somewhat quaint concepts of the universe, but on his own. In deference to Tycho Brahe's wishes, however, he called them the Rudolphine Tables in honor of the Emperor Rudolf II.

Kepler's work set the seal on the heliocentric view of the universe. But the triumph of his genius was not only ill rewarded, it had an almost baleful influence on the closing years of his life. Tycho Brahe's heirs hounded him for their share of any profits accruing from the publication of the Rudolphine Tables, and his patrons omitted to pay him what they owed. Duke Albrecht von Wallenstein (1583–1634), the German general who commanded the Imperial armies in the Thirty Years' War, actually employed Kepler as his astrologer, but in the end paid him not one cent for his astrological services.

Part Two: 2

KEPLER'S major achievements in the field of astronomy tend naturally to overshadow his contributions to optics. Yet so numerous and so fruitful were these that many regard him as the founder of dioptrics. He owed much to Galileo who sent him a copy of his *Messenger from the Stars* thereby stimulating in him a curiosity to scan the heavens as Galileo himself had done. He constructed a telescope with which to catch a glimpse of the marvels but felt disappointed because the telescopic field was so small and its powers of magnification so inadequate. He realized that the Dutch telescope had somehow to be improved if he was to get better results. He found valuable clues in the way the human eye functions. Was not the eye an optical instrument? The retinal image had to be inverted in the animal or human eye, as Christoph Scheiner had demonstrated. If it was not inverted then the objects would appear upside down. Kepler understood the principle of the Critical Angle without grasping the general Law of Refraction. He first explained how spectacles corrected defects of eyesight, such as long and short sights: they helped the eye's refracting surfaces to sharpen the image of an object upon the retina.

Let us consider now, in the light of modern knowledge, how the human eye functions. The eye is one of the most important organs we have because such a vast amount of information reaches us through our sense of sight. Kepler appreciated that the eye was itself an optical instrument. We may fairly compare it to a highly sensitive camera; yet it is truly far more sensitive, accurate, and flexible, than any camera so far devised. The eye can take an unlimited number of "snaps" in color for the mind to classify and to store up for future reference. It can take close-ups and long-distance shots.

The *iris* controls the amount of light which penetrates the eye, acting like the shutter of a camera. It has an "aperture," which to admit more light grows bigger and to shut it out grows smaller. Located in front of the lens, the iris is a highly transparent, biconvex body, almost spherical in shape, resembling a little doughnut. The function of the lens is to focus light rays on the retina, the area at the back of the eye which is highly sensitive to light. Certain chemicals are responsible for the retina's sensitivity to light. They alter as light strikes. *Rhodopsin,* known also as Visual Purple, is one of these chemicals and it contains a plentiful supply of vitamin A. Near the center of the retina is the *fovea,* an area in which nerve endings called *cones* are concentrated. Cones enable us to have direct vision and to tell both the color and the intensity of the light. Close to the fovea, and also in parts of the retina, are other nerve endings, known as *rods,* which, although they cannot much help us to detect color, are extremely sensitive to light, so much so that they can hardly perform their functions in very bright light.

The *ciliary body* helps the eye to adapt to the various situations that confront it. It is a round structure, triangular in cross-section, placed immediately behind the iris, and it contains the *ciliary muscle.* The ciliary body supports between sixty and eighty paired strands of suspensory fibers connected to the lens. These fibers are tense even when they are at rest, and they pull the lens into a flattened shape. When the ciliary muscle contracts, the ciliary body pulls inward toward the lens, giving the lens a more convex shape.

In this cunning fashion nature has provided us with the convex shape of the lens which is suitable for seeing objects at close range.

The Arab scholar Althazen thought that an image was registered independently in each eye but that it became a single image in the *optic nerve.*

The optic nerve is the second cranial nerve, which connects retina and brain and conducts to the brain sensory impulses of what we see so that it can "instruct" us how to identify them and distinguish them from each other. Thus eye muscles and not the optic nerve enable the eyes to converge, to assume such a position that each eye can present to the brain the very same picture. Indeed, if we try to see something very close up we begin to squint. This is because the eyes have to converge excessively in order to see too near. We are able to judge distance by judging unconsciously the degree to which our eyes converge when fixed upon any object.

Such details about the way in which the eye operates were, of course, unknown to Kepler. Yet he advanced the correct theory of vision and, assisted by mathematical advances, a theory of dioptrics. Mathematics had received a shot in the arm when Vieta (1540–1603) turned all algebra into argument by symbol, employing letters for quantities both known and unknown. He extended his idea to trigonometry and thus enormously speeded up calculations. Simon Stevin (1548–1620), in 1585, showed how decimals could be used and, in 1614, the Scotsman John Napier introduced logarithms. The Dutchman Willebrord Snellius or Snell (1591–1626) clarified the Law of Sines which had mystified scholars since about the second century.

The purpose of observations by astronomers was to plot in advance the paths of heavenly bodies. Where would the sun, or the moon, be on a certain day three years hence? To make such calculations, angles had to be measured and beyond mere measurement of angles there had to be a mathematical process for the application of data about angles.

Hipparchus, a dyed-in-the-wool geocentric, the most influential astronomer of the ancient world, who lived either at Rhodes or at Alexandria, is thought to have been the creator of trigonometry (measurement of triangles), as well as of positional astronomy. In his trigonometry, every angle taken to be at the center of a circle with a radius of 1, was represented by the chord subtended by its arc. Al Battani, an Arab mathematician of the ninth century A.D. used the semichord of the double arc instead of the chord. This semichord was the *sine*. Al Battani added to it the *cosine*. Abul-Wefa, during the tenth century, added the *tangent* and the *secant*.

Thus Arab scholars were the real creators of modern trigonometry, a branch of mathematics that deals with problems relating to plane and spherical triangles. Its principles are based on the fixed proportions of angles and sides in a right-angled triangle. Since trigonometry is of importance to surveyors, we can see why Snell was impelled to better it, for he was a "father of geodesy," which is the aspect of mathematics concerned with the figure and area of the earth, or large parts of it.

The "heart" of the microscope is its convex lens, because anything we look at through a convex lens appears larger to our eyes. Indeed, the story of the microscope is virtually the story of the convex lens. The simple microscope, or "single" microscope, as it was once called, has only one lens whereas the compound, or "double," microscope has two lenses or combinations: *objective* and *ocular*. An *ocular,* or *eye piece* (from the Latin *oculus*: eye), consists of one, or more than one, lens, or system of lenses, which, acting together with the eye, helps to magnify the image formed by the objective. The *objective* is a lens (of which there are various kinds), or system of lenses, which provides an enlarged, inverted image of any object we wish to subject to microscopic scrutiny. We have put the matter very simply, giving its bare essentials. Systems or combinations of lenses are employed in order to try to neutralize certain faults, or *aberrations,* that simple lenses possess. We shall, in due course, see how scientists overcome these aberrations. It took them a very long time.

The so-called Holland glass, or Dutch compound, microscope includes a convex lens for an objective and a concave ocular. The so-called Kepler compound also includes a convex lens for an objective, but it has another convex lens for an ocular, because when Kepler considered the Dutch compound microscope, he quickly saw that he could obtain the same effect by making both objective and ocular convex. The difference was that the *virtual* image would be inverted. With the Dutch compound, however, the concave ocular served as amplifier for the objective and the virtual image was therefore erect. The term *virtual image,* contrasting with *real image,* deserves explanation. A *real image* is formed by a lens or optical instrument when the object is placed outside or beyond the principal center of focus. It is called a real image because it forms a picture of an object without any help from the eye. It is the kind of picture, for example, that enables us to take photographs or films and then project them on a screen. A *virtual image* is an "imaginary" one because the real image is produced by the rays of light that, whenever an object is scrutinized, must pass from object to eye. It is these rays that form the image on the retina as they strike the eye. To construct a virtual image, the object must be located at a point somewhere between the principal focus and the lens.

Simplifying considerably, the real image is "performed" for the eye, whereas the virtual image is formed within the eye itself. A few more observations might clarify the principles upon which telescopes and microscopes operate. The nearer an object to the chief point of focus, the more distant the image. The nearer the image to the chief point of focus, the more distant from it must be the object. Put it another way, the closer to the principal focus the object, the more distant from that point the image, and the relatively larger its size. This applies both to real and virtual images.

Kepler set out his optical theories in his *Dioptrica* and showed the principles upon which telescopes and microscopes might be constructed. He said, for example, that objects could be displayed both magnified and erect by combining three convex lenses. Here was the basis of the *erecting,* or *terrestrial,* telescope. And, as we have already mentioned, Kepler first drew attention to the eye as a piece of optical equipment, pointing out that the retinal image had to be inverted if objects were not to appear upside down. His replacement of the concave eye piece by a convex one constituted a significant advance and his instrument was the authentic forerunner of modern optical apparatus. Galileo's telescope remained essentially an opera or field glass while Kepler's developed into the true astronomical refractor, the ancestor of many modern ones, including the giant at the Yerkes Observatory near Chicago, whose object glass is a biconvex lens some 40 inches across.

The Jesuit, Christoph Scheiner, had more practical ability than Kepler and, by implementing Kepler's plan, built the first true "astronomical" refractor. Scheiner employed telescope and microscope both for observation and for projecting real images. He showed how the *camera obscura* could be used for investigating the sun, especially sunspots. In his *Rosa Ursina,* he echoes Galileo when he tells us that by using two convex lenses, as Kepler advised, "a fly was made as large as an elephant and a flea to the size of a camel." Galileo is reported to have seen flies, with hair on their legs, as big as young lambs. The reason for this was that early microscopes were in effect short-focus telescopes. Had Galileo wished to use one of his smaller telescopes as a microscope he would have had to lengthen it a good deal in order to get an image of a near object. Not until the telescope objective had been changed for one of much shorter focal length did the microscope come into its own.

The practical talents of Christoph Scheiner were considerable, but there are two other contenders for honors in the field: an Austrian Franciscan, Schyrle (or Schyrlaeus) of Rheita (1597–1660), and Nicola Zucchi (1586–1670), an Italian Jesuit who was an associate of Scheiner's. In 1616, Zucchi devised the reflecting telescope by putting a concave mirror where the object glass was sited. Rheita made an erecting eye piece for the terrestrial telescope. Zucchi's idea, which Newton was to take up, enabled the image to be reflected into the eye piece and to be magnified. On the other hand, the telescope was itself often called a "Rheita," which tells us the place in the history of the telescope that contemporary opinion accorded to the Austrian Franciscan.

Part Two: 3

THE hardness of the diamond has from earliest times been appreciated by craftsmen who, just as we ourselves do, used it as a cutter. And just as we also do, they used emery, a crystalline mineral, or fine sand, for abrading, or "scraping down." For centuries the art of lens grinding remained almost unaltered, although the work of Galileo and his pupil, Evangelista Torricelli (1608–47), had helped to spread the knowledge of it. As lens makers strove to attain greater powers of magnification, they realized that both their equipment and their methods were inadequate. They had three chief aims: to make the curvature of the glass disk as accurate as possible, to plane it perfectly, and to produce glass that was crystal clear and without the tiresome imperfections they found so hard to exclude.

Curvature depended upon the skill of the hands. So did

polishing and shaping. Lens makers had the simplest of machines to help them, none driven by power. They labored at grinding blank glass to shape by means of a convex or concave half-disk that was fixed to the workbench. There were times when a fresh tool had to be substituted during the course of the work because wear and tear reduced its efficiency. Accuracy was the most vexing problem. Iron tools were generally forged, and bronze ones cast and turned on a lathe whose shortcomings militated against accuracy. The craftsman found himself tired out, his hands stiff and painful as a result of pressing the glass blank down hard with the fingers against the tool. Sometimes he spared the fingers by cementing a little handle to the glass blank with which he could hold it and press down.

To prevent cloudiness and to keep the surface scratch-free presented many difficulties. Glass was composed chiefly of soda, lime, and silica; lead, potash, and barium were not then, as they are now, common ingredients. Soda (sodium oxide) was added to lower the melting point, which makers seemed unable to ascertain. Any excess of it induced cloudiness. Even during the seventeenth century, glass was indiffently polished and figured. Its poor quality made the production of high quality lenses almost impossible. Flaws and bubbles were too common to permit the manufacture of objects for large telescopes. No wonder Zucchi was driven to try to reflect the image into the eye piece. The property of reflection possessed by certain metals had been noted by the ancients, who turned out metallic mirrors or made them of glass backed with a reflecting metal.

In 1515, Peder Mänsson, a Swedish metallurgist, gave an

account of applying tin to glass with mercury. An Italian, Vanoccio (1480–1539), author of a celebrated book on metallurgy entitled *Pirotechnica,* refers to treating glass with antimony. However, most mirrors were of metal, and a chemist, Johann Rudolph Glauber (1604–68), not only told how they were cast but dealt exhaustively with the kinds of metals used. As a rule some hard metal was chosen as more suitable for polishing. Glauber advised a copper-tin-arsenic mixture but warned against overdoing the copper because it reddened the surface whereas the essential of a good mirror was a white sheen. J. A. Pantheus, a metallurgist (circa 1530), recommended silver for this very reason, and he expressed his preference for metal over glass because glass was too easily breakable.

As astrolabes, quadrants, and sun dials, gave way to the new marvels among optical instruments, manufacturers inevitably faced many technical difficulties in their endeavours to meet the growing demand. An expanding industry faced a shortage of craftsmen, such as metalworkers, turners, and glassworkers, who simply had to be borrowed from other trades. Thus instrument makers linked up with spectacle makers, clock makers and other London companies. Gradually their premises became far more than centers of manufacture, they became shops where they sold not only their own, but also other makes of apparatus to eager customers in search of better and better equipment.

Scientists, keen amateurs, and craftsmen rubbed shoulders and exchanged scientific and technical information. Robert Hooke (1635–1703), Curator of Experiments at the Royal Society in London, has left us descriptions of what

The astrolabe was used for taking altitudes. Trained on the sun, for example, it could measure angular height above the horizon. Accordingly, time of day could be estimated. Alidade (from an Arabic word meaning *revolving radius*) was an "indicator arm," showing the number of degrees of the arc. Astrolabe, armillary sphere and wall quadrant were all essentially instruments for measuring angles. They had a forerunner in the Alexandrian *plinth*, from which they derive.

happened at such meetings, impromptu or arranged. Scientists, following the example of Galileo, who had had his own workshops, did a great deal of their own work, grinding lenses and spending considerable time building parts for their apparatus. Robert Hooke, René Descartes (1596–1650), Christiaan Huygens (1629–95), Isaac Newton (1642–1727), and Antony van Leeuwenhoek (1632–1723), all famous in the sphere of optics (we shall be dealing fully with them), were great craftsmen as well as great scientists. They had mastered the art of lens grinding.

Expansion of the optical industry also led to specialization. The all-arounder was displaced by the craftsman adept at one particular aspect of his trade. Each manufacturer earned a reputation for his prowess in a certain department. Thus, the Italian Eustachio Divini (1620–95) and the Englishman Christopher Cock were known for their telescope objectives. Cock, who kept a shop at Long Acre in London, made a microscope for Hooke that is on view at the Science Museum at South Kensington, London.

Of the many problems that the manufacturers of optical instruments had to try to resolve, the first concerned design. How could the optical parts be housed to their best advantage? How were components to be improved? Stability left much to be desired, and though a tripod arrangement went some way toward steadying instruments, real stability was not achieved until the eighteenth century. Often any adjustments of the eye piece tended to throw the object out of focus and, generally speaking, focusing and direction were inadequate. Tubes had to be made very precisely for sliding in order to focus. Galileo had used lead for his first tubes.

Later manufacturers tried rolled parchment or pasteboard in various colors, often gilded and decorated by craftsmen who had been trained in bookbinding. The first brass instrument was not produced in England until 1742. If a very long tube happened to be required, it sometimes consisted of four wooden planks joined together in a square, to which eye piece and objective were lashed or strapped. "Aerial" telescopes often had their objectives fixed on a tower or pole and they were manipulated by ropes or cords. The viewer had at his disposal a detachable eye piece.

The long telescope — and some were over 100 feet long — represented a way of reducing spherical aberration. Spherical aberration and chromatic aberration remained for years two of the most serious drawbacks in optics. Spherical aberrations occurred because only those rays of light that passed through the lens near the center converged at a focus. Somehow those rays that did not converge had to be excluded and this was achieved by stopping down the lens. Chromatic aberration (*chroma* is the Greek word for *color*) occurred because the lens was inclined to behave like a prism and break up light into its colors around the edges. The fringes of the image thus became shiny and blurred.

Hooke pointed out how difficult it was to ascertain precisely the true shape of the object, "the same object seeming quite different in one position to the light, from what it really is, and may be discovered in another." He claimed he examined his specimens over and over before drawing what he took to be their true appearance. To obtain clear definition seemed almost impossible; it seemed out of the question to grind lenses with the nonspherical curvature that theory demanded. The only way to reduce spherical and chromatic aberrations was to make lenses that were less curved. And if they were made less curved the focal distance was lengthened.

Descartes is said to have designed a microscope that was the forerunner to the Lieberkuhn, which was so popular until the 1880's, and he is said also to have put forward a proposal for overcoming spherical aberration, although he seems never to have translated it into practical terms. Evidently he promised to turn out a lens of such perfection that it would be possible to discern life on the moon (if any), and also the shapes of its animals (again, if any).

Part Two: 4

RENÉ DESCARTES was born in 1596 in the Touraine, the "garden of France," and was educated by Jesuits. He was astonishingly precocious and he decided he would concentrate on only those subjects that might be capable of exact proof. That exact proof he himself wished to furnish. He intended to seek the knowlege that nature alone could offer. He served in the army of Prince Maurice of Nassau, and while traveling on the Continent, he believed that he, like St. Paul on the road to Damascus, had "seen the light." Accordingly he made up his mind to apply the "certainties" of mathematics to science and to metaphysics. Because of the hold the Church exerted on French intellectual life, and the danger of challenging religious beliefs, he departed, in 1629, for the more liberal atmosphere of Holland where he hoped for greater freedom of thought. In 1649, he visited the court of Queen Christina of Sweden. He was in Stockholm when he died in 1650.

Descartes approached every proposition through his method of doubt: taking for granted *nothing* except the things that to him seemed self-evident — "clear and distinct" — and the things that could be rigorously deduced from these "clear and distinct" propositions. But in the long run, he, like his most illustrious predecessors, was trying to form a picture of the world based upon suppositions in advance. That these suppositions were his rather than theirs made little difference: scientific theory should be derived from the facts yielded by observations, rather than the other way around. Nevertheless, his was a new departure, an attitude that marked a real break with the thinking of the old world. He saw the universe as composed of "ether," or "ethereal fluid," swirling everlastingly about a center, as does a whirlpool, or a hurricane. Particles of the "ethereal fluid" could penetrate all matter because they were infinitely small.

A ray of light was these particles in vibration. Disturbed in some unknown fashion at some unknown point of illumination, it traveled to the eye, which reacted to its presence. Influenced by metaphysical thought Descartes conceived of light as "pressure" in the medium it was traversing. He believed also that the denser the medium through which light passed, the higher the velocity of the light. Thus, it would travel faster through water than through air. His countryman, the mathematician Pierre Fermat (1601–55), with whom he had a number of famous disputes, opposed such views because, he argued, nature's work is done in the simplest, most direct way. When a ray of light moves between two points it does so in the shortest possible time by taking the shortest possible route. Both the Law of Reflection and the fact that light travels in straight lines underlined this principle.

Descartes was the first scientist to provide in his *Dioptrique* (1637) a system of optics founded upon mechanical considerations. He declared that the Angle of Reflection and the Angle of Incidence were equal, and he suggested that a water tube ought to reduce, if not altogether eliminate, spherical aberration. He published, some time after Willebrord Snell's death, the Law of Refraction, which the latter had proposed in 1621.

As we already know, refraction is the change in direction when light passes from one medium (for example, air) into another (for example, water), causing the bent-stick effect we notice in ponds. The degree of bending, or change of direction, depends not only upon the relative density of the two mediums, but upon the angle at which the light rays strike. The greater the difference in density between the two mediums and the more oblique the angle at which the rays enter, the greater the refraction. The sine, and the corresponding angle, are greater in a rare medium than in a dense one. Thus, a ray entering a denser medium from a rarer one at a *lesser* angle bends *toward* the normal. By contrast, a ray entering a rarer medium from a denser one at a *greater* angle bends *from* the normal.

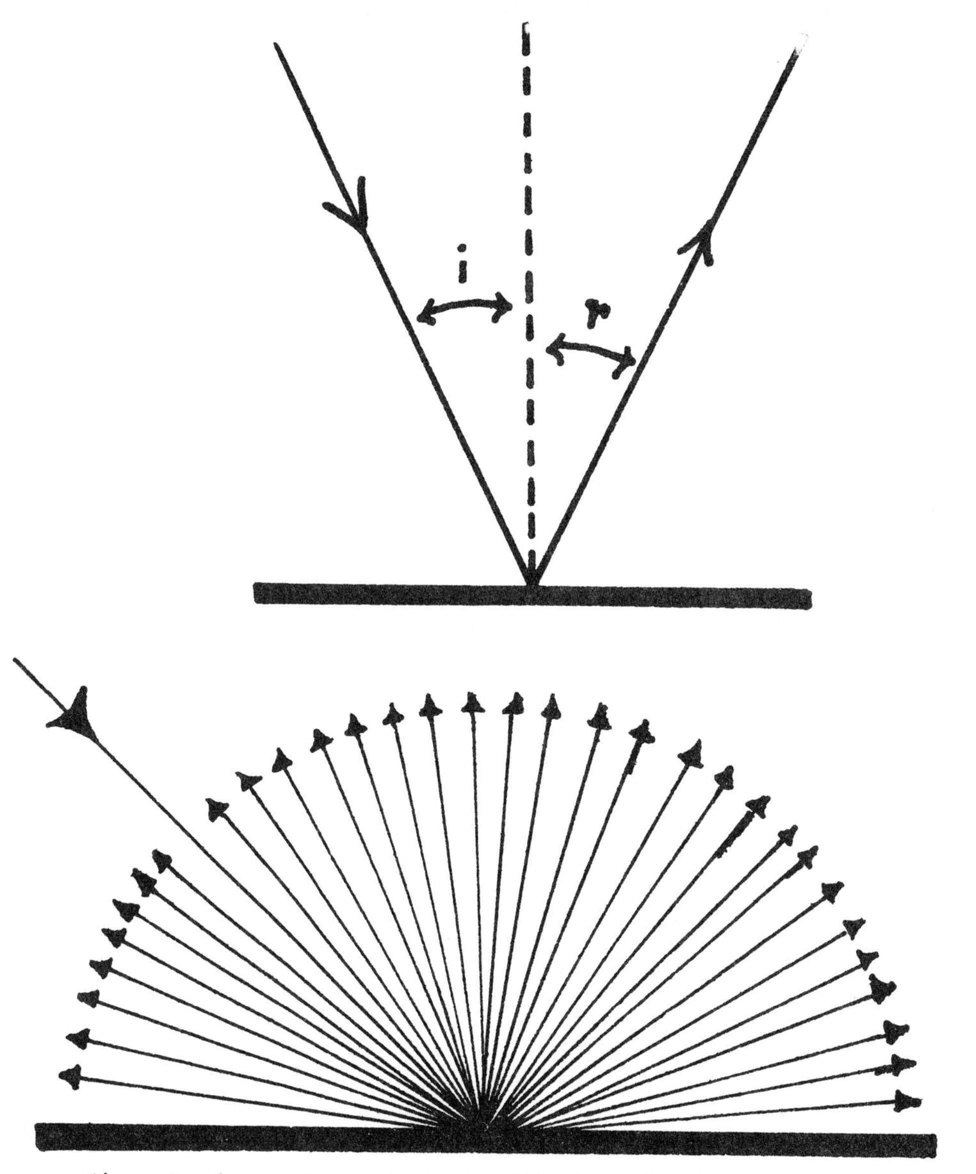

Above: Regular or mirror reflection in which the angle of incidence, i, is equal to the angle of reflection, r.
Below: Irregular or diffuse reflection. A ray of light striking a rough surface, a piece of white paper, for example, is scattered almost equally in all directions, making a hemisphere.

For those interested, the mathematical formula for the Sine Law of Snell and Descartes, as we call it, is:

$$\frac{\sin i}{\sin r} = \text{Index of Refraction}$$

where *i* stands for the incident ray and *r* the refracted ray.

In simple words, the sine of the angle made by the incident ray with the normal to the separating surface, divided by the sine of the angle made by the refracting ray with its normal, gives us the relative direction of the ray in its two mediums, or its Index of Refraction. In due course, Robert Hooke devised equipment for measuring refractive indices and was accordingly able to verify Snell's Law with considerable accuracy.

The theoretical basis of optics was growing firmer with such discoveries. Before Newton's day, an Italian professor of mathematics at Bologna University, Francesco Grimaldi (1613–63), experimented intensively to determine the nature of light. The majority of scientists had the idea that light traveled in straight lines — that it could not "bend" around obstacles, in the same way as sound waves or water waves. Grimaldi observed that when he shone a thin beam of light on some fine opaque object, the shadow cast was wider than it should have been according to calculations. In addition, the shadow was fringed by colors.

Two years after Grimaldi's death, a book of his was published, in which he spoke of light as some kind of vibration which — if he could believe the evidence of his experiments

— did "bend" into the shadow. Indeed, how could the bending of light rays, and the coloring at the edge of shadow, be explained without casting aside the straight-line theory and assuming that light, after all, did travel in waves, such as those we might get if we dropped a pebble into a pond? The colors, he thought, resulted from changing wave lengths. Each color had its own wave length, just as each note of music also has its own wave-length. Nevertheless, Grimaldi did not advance a wave theory of light supported by mathematical proof; he only gave an account of diffraction, the breakup of a beam of light into a series of dark and light bands or color spectra.

Did light, then, travel in waves? And at what speed? These were the two questions that demanded answers. The second of them was answered first. In the 1660's, Paris was a brilliant center of science. In Paris, and elsewhere in France also, scientific gatherings took place, attended not only by French scholars, but by their colleagues from abroad. Out of such gatherings grew the Royal Academy of Sciences, for whose foundation Jean-Baptiste Colbert (1619–83), Louis XIV's Chief Minister, obtained his monarch's blessing. Two rooms were provided in the Royal Library for the use of members and attracted many distinguished foreigners like Christiaan Huygens; Giovanni Domenico Cassini (1625–1712), professor of astronomy at the University of Bologna in Italy (where Copernicus himself had studied a century and a half earlier); and Ole Roemer (1644–1710), a Dane born at Aarhus near Copenhagen. Roemer had been brought to France by the Abbé Jean

Picard (1620–83), a French priest who by geodetic triangulation measured a meridian arc between Paris and Amiens. Roemer stayed with Picard in his quarters at the Observatory until Colbert took him up at the age of twenty-eight to make him a member of the Academy. He was also private tutor to the Dauphin and was well rewarded for his services.

Roemer occupied himself particularly with the behavior of Jupiter's satellites, long regarded by astronomers as "signals" from the heavens, that, if interpreted properly, could yield considerable enlightenment. One of the satellites might, for example, be concealed by Jupiter's disk, or one might be lying "on top" of another so that the two presented themselves as one. Since such events could be predicted they served as a sort of clock. Indeed, it was possible to tell the time by them in any part of our hemisphere. Roemer was quite familiar with such matters but in consulting his tables, he found that his own observations did not tally.

He noted that when the earth stood between the sun and Jupiter, eclipses took place later. Roemer asked himself why. He decided that he could account for the difference he had detected in one way only. He argued that light had to travel farther when the earth moved away from Jupiter and that it had to travel a lesser distance when the earth drew closer to Jupiter. He concluded, therefore, that light had a finite velocity.

In November, 1675, he announced his discovery to the Academy, with a certain amount of caution for it was generally believed that the speed of light was infinite. Roemer said that, according to his calculations, the differences in the times taken for light from Jupiter to reach the earth equaled the time taken for light to travel the distance between the earth's nearer and farther positions in its orbit around the sun. This distance he estimated to be some 69,500,000 leagues, and light traversed it in some twenty-two minutes. If this were so, the speed of light was 52,650 leagues (about 130,900 miles) per second.

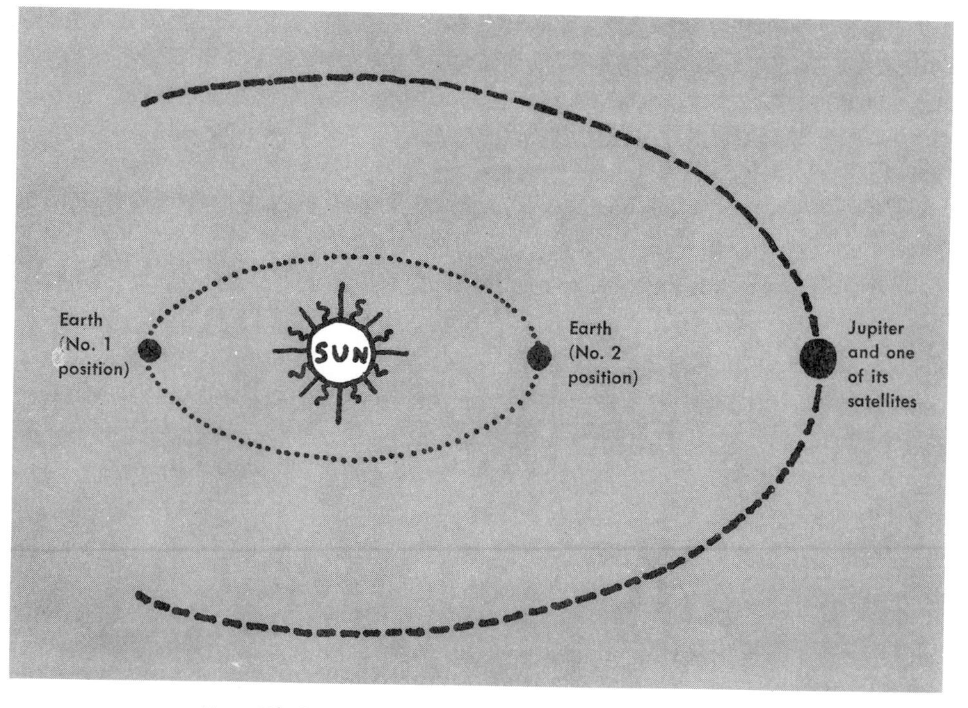

How Ole Roemer worked out the speed of light:
When our Earth is in position 1, the image of Jupiter takes longer to reach us than when our Earth is in position 2, and position 2 is twice the distance between Earth and the sun. With the knowledge of the time taken for the image of Jupiter to reach positions 1 and 2, Roemer could calculate the speed of light.

By one of those neat, simple deductions which have repeatedly proved their value to science, Roemer had worked out the speed of light. His figures have since been proved incorrect, for today we know that light traverses the distance between the two positions of the earth's orbit in sixteen minutes, not in twenty-two minutes as Roemer said, and that its velocity is 186,000 miles per second, not 130,900 miles. Nevertheless, Roemer's feat far surpasses correctness of figures because of its demonstration that the speed of light was not infinite but finite and therefore measurable.

In 1679, Roemer visited England and met Newton; Newton's friend, Edmund Halley (1656–1742), the astronomer who observed the comet that was named after him; and John Flamsteed (1646–1719), the first Astronomer-Royal of England who took systematic observations from Greenwich Observatory, London, where some of his apparatus remains on view. Galileo had suspected that the speed of light was finite and measurable, yet many leading scholars doubted Roemer's claim. The Dutchman Christiaan Huygens and these three Englishmen were exceptions.

Some two years after the announcement of his discovery, Roemer was back in his native Copenhagen trying to improve his friend the Abbé Picard's telescope. The best available star map of the times had been drawn up in 1661 by Johannes Höwelke, known better as Hevelius (1611–87), whose home was at Danzig. His father was a wealthy brewer so he had both the money and the time to indulge his passion for astronomy. He was even able to build himself an observatory which consisted of several towers with revolving roofs put up on top of his house. In it he had the usual range of equipment including a 16-foot-long telescope, and beneath the observatory he had installed a printing press with which to record his observations. His *Machina Coelestis,* a superbly illustrated volume, is on view at the Paris Observatory. The remarkable feature of Hevelius's star map was that he had drawn it up according to observations made with the naked eye. He only used divided circles fitted with alidades, or "indicator arms," showing the degrees cut off on the arc. Halley wondered how accurate Hevelius's naked-eye observations were. In the company of Hevelius one day, he suggested they should both observe stars at the same time, he, Halley, with a telescope. Halley was astounded to find that Hevelius could be as accurate without a telescope as he was with one.

Clearly Hevelius' powers were unique, but sooner or later the telescope was bound to replace the alidade. For the changeover, the Abbé Picard, Roemer's friend, was largely responsible. He introduced the telescope for sightings in positional astronomy and augmented its accuracy, replacing alidade with a webwork of fine lines in the focal plane of the object glass. At the Paris Observatory, the Abbé Picard fitted divided circles with telescopes and also constructed a quadrant about 5 feet in radius and set it against the wall in such a way that the telescope covered the meridian. Thus, he could calculate correctly the ascension of stars from the time they started to move across the meridian and could tell the instant at which the meridian was traversed.

Roemer bettered Picard's instrument by producing his transit-telescope, which was so installed that it could traverse a horizontal axis in the plane of the meridian. It was thus possible to watch the transit of any heavenly body across the meridian as it moved through a wire web set at the focus of the eye piece. He also invented the micrometer with the aid of his astronomer friend, Adrien Auzout (1630–91). The micrometer was operated according to a thread-and-screw principle, and the screw was set in the focal plane of the telescope's eye piece so that the distance between two objects in view could be measured, even the diameter of a planet.

The moment that Roemer and Auzout announced that they had transformed the reticle (the network of thin lines in the focal plane of the object glass, which took the place of the alidade) into the micrometer by making one of the vertical hairlines movable through the turn of a screw, English scholars raised their voices in protest. The micrometer, they claimed, had long ago been invented by William Gascoigne (1612–44), who had chosen to keep the invention to himself. It may be that Gascoigne has a claim, yet he had only himself to blame for having failed to make public his device. Roemer and Auzout invented their micrometer quite independently of Gascoigne and lose no credit for having done so later than he did.

About 1665, open sights were being abandoned for telescopic sights. Robert Hooke produced a number of measuring devices that made open sights far less necessary. However instrument manufacturers continued to face difficulties in trying to achieve mechanical precision in dividing and reading scales. Moreover, they were struggling to discover accurate ways of measuring time. Gradually, clock-driven telescopes began coming into fashion, Following up

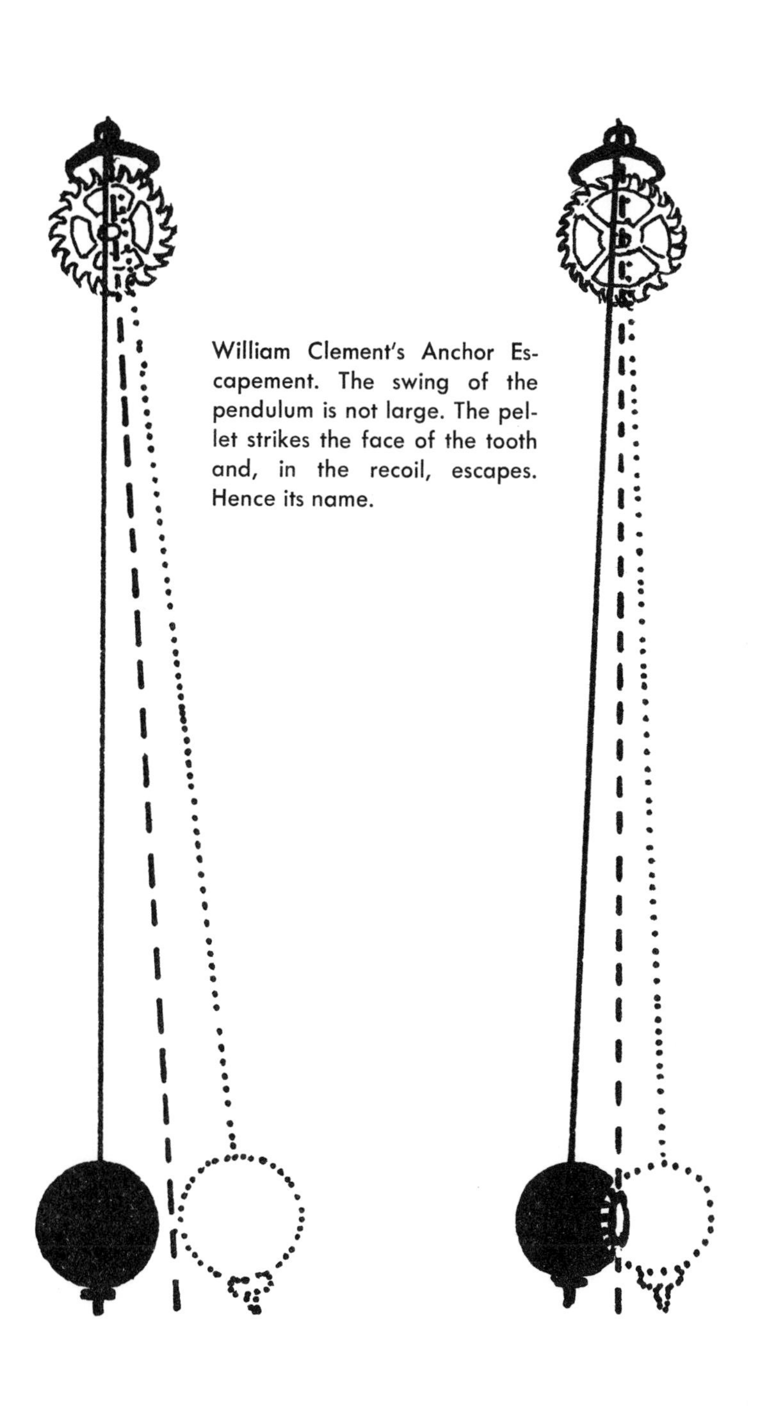

William Clement's Anchor Escapement. The swing of the pendulum is not large. The pellet strikes the face of the tooth and, in the recoil, escapes. Hence its name.

an idea suggested by Galileo's son, Christiaan Huygens demonstrated how the fall of the weight in the balance wheel escapement of the seventeenth-century clock could be purged of its irregularities. A swinging pendulum was the corrective since it was the erratic fall of the weight that caused the trouble and the swinging pendulum largely obviated it. In 1675, he published his account of the spiral watch spring, which led to Robert Hooke's anchor escapement.

The English clock maker William Clement adopted Hooke's device and turned out a wonderful piece of machinery which ensured that a clock would lose no more than a single second during the course of a twenty-four-hour day. The science of horology had come a long way from the hourglass, the sun dial, and the mechanical clocks housed in the towers of European cathedrals. These cathedral clocks may have been splendid artistic creations but were indifferent timekeepers, for they gained or lost a whole hour and more within the course of the twenty-four-hour day.

Part Two: 5

CHRISTIAAN HUYGENS, the son of an influential personage in the suite of the Prince of Orange, had shown such an amazing aptitude for mathematics that Descartes himself had assigned him problems to resolve. His father, who was in touch with several leading men of art and science, encouraged his family to mingle with cultivated and distinguished minds and Christiaan, like his brothers, took advantage of the many opportunities that came his way to do so. In 1655, Christiaan visited Paris, the "center of the world," returning there to stay from 1666 to 1681. An aristocrat, he kept away from the essentially aristocratic French society in which he might reasonably have been expected to move and sought instead the companionship of poets, artists and scientists. They welcomed him into their circles not just because he was wealthy and able to extend them his patronage, but because he was really one of them. Already, he had built a remarkable telescope whose object glass had a focal distance of 12 feet, and located the satellite of Saturn which we now know as Titan.

The brothers Huygens, Christiaan and Constantijn, were master opticians and ground their own long-focus lenses and object glasses. Samples of their work, signed with a diamond by one or the other, are on exhibition at Leyden in Holland, in Brussels, and in London. The brothers next turned out an object glass with a focal distance of 21 feet and, encouraged by their success, they went on to bigger things. They ground lenses with focuses of 40, 50, and even 62 feet. This last, 5.8 inches across, and signed by Constantijn, is on exhibition at Brussels University.

In 1655, Christiaan Huygens returned home from France to discover the Rings of Saturn, using an object glass of 21 feet. The appearance of Saturn had long puzzled astronomers because it looked as though it were divided in two by a black band. Huygens's splendid observations of the planet's rings would immediately have relieved their minds except that he judged it safer to announce his discovery in the form of an anagram, afraid perhaps of repercussions from the religious-minded. It was almost three years before he finally decided to provide the key to his original anagram.

Christiaan Huygens's great refracting telescopes were in many ways among the marvels of the day. Very-long-focus instruments could not simply be picked up by the hand and held before the eye, nor could they be rested on a tripod or window sill as was often done. They had to be hung by a cord that circled a fixed pully at the summit of a pole or mast. The user was thus able to point at the object he wished to sight. In some cases telescopes were tubeless because of their great focal distance. The eye piece was fixed to one end of a rod, and the objective to the other.

Since this type of equipment was inclined to bend before every wind, the focal distance could not very well be increased further without inventing some different mode of installation. But the Huygens brothers increased the focal distance to 80, 100, and even 150 feet. Constantijn put his signature on one lens, now in the possession of the Royal Society, with a diameter of 9.4 inches and a focal distance of 224 feet. But it was Christiaan who, in 1683, found the way to employ lenses of such size. The object glass within its tube was fixed at one end of a metal rod which rested on a shelf which could slide up and down a mast. The eye piece, also riveted to a metal rod, was attached by a length of wire to the rod carrying the objective. So long as the length of wire or cord was stretched tight, the two lenses could be brought exactly opposite each other. But the truth was that ingenuity had far outpaced practicabality in such instruments.

During the early 1670's, Christiaan Huygens, then living in Paris, left the laborious work of lens grinding to his brother Constantijn, and had even abandoned his surveillance of the heavens. This task he left to men like Giovanni Domenico Cassini, the Italian who lived in France and who was an illustrious member of the French Academy of Sciences. Cassini had, in 1672, taken up his quarters at the Paris Observatory where, according to Huygens, he "never lets a lucid night go by without contemplating the heavens;

Huygens, Herschel, Cassini and other astronomers built many large, often ingenious outdoor telescopes. Here is one of Huygens' great refracting instruments. Eyepiece and object glass were joined by a cord which, if kept fully tensed, made certain that eyepiece and object glass faced each other exactly.

to which I have no wish to subject myself since I am content to rest upon the laurels of my former discoveries which may well be worth all made since." About thirty-three years before Cassini arrived in France he declared that Mars, like our own earth, was spinning around on its axis and that it took 24 hours, 40 minutes, for the planet to complete one rotation. The correct figure is 24 hours, 37 minutes, 23 seconds, so we can applaud Cassini for having got so close to it with primitive equipment. His telescope, according to one account, "cannot have given him an image much larger than a shilling seen from a distance of forty yards." An ophthalmic expert, it is said, thought that as an observer Cassini was infallible, possessed of an eye quite free from astigmatism and a retina of extreme sensitivity.

Cassini, received everywhere like a prince, lived like a prince. He abandoned his Italian nationality, became a Frenchman, and to mark it married a French girl. He settled down with her in a château where their children were born, to start off the new line of French Cassinis. While he enjoyed the life of the gentleman, he remained, nevertheless, always devoted to astronomy. He was a zealous and dutiful observer of the heavens; night after night he was to be found in the Observatory, peering through one of Huygens's outsize telescopes, or through lenses ground by those master opticians of France, Pierre Borel and Le Bas. Borel's eye piece of 3-inch focus magnified 120 to 140 times.

But Cassini could not be satisfied with such average excellence. He used a 70-foot instrument with a triangular tube, looking as though it were made up of three ladders, which he had hung by cords from a pole. Wishing to use object glasses more than 100 feet long, Cassini followed up Huygens's idea of the tubeless telescope and had a wooden tower some 118 feet high transported to the Observatory, where he supervised its installation on a foundation of masonry. It had a staircase, a balcony, and a hoist; and the viewer standing below with the eye piece in his hand gazed through the object glass at the top of the tower. This expensive and perhaps whimsical astronomical machine cost a great deal of money and took some three years to construct. Its focus was about 150 feet, its diameter was about 9 feet, and it magnified about 600 times. Yet there seem to have been doubts about its usefulness because observations through it may well have been hindered by the somewhat obscuring airs over Paris.

Cassini's remarkable eyesight, and his zeal and patience, were fully rewarded, for within the space of a dozen or more years he was credited with the discovery of four of Saturn's five satellites: Iapetus, Rhea, Tethys, and Dione. He also noticed that the Ring of Saturn was divided in two by a dark band which interposed itself between bright and dark rings. Naturally enough this dark band was named Cassini's Division.

Solar parallax, the angle at the sun subtended by the radius of our earth, made the distance between sun and earth hard to measure precisely. The Italian Giambaptista Riccioli (1598–1671) estimated it to be more than 24,000,000 miles.Next, Flamsteed estimated it to be at least 84,000,000 miles by determining that the solar parallax was no more than 10 seconds of the arc. Cassini himself tackled the problem and declared that the distance was 87,000,000 miles.

Until well into the eighteenth century, this sort of figure was generally accepted, comparing with our own of 92,800,000 miles.

When Roemer announced that light had a finite velocity and gave his figure for its speed, Cassini opposed him. Cassini sided with the viewpoint of Descartes rather than with that of Fermat. But what was light? Was it "pressure" as Descartes thought? And how did it travel? The second question called for an answer: how *did* light travel? In 1690, Christiaan Huygens published his *Traité de la Lumière* (*Treatise on Light*) in which he described the motion of light. Light, he said, traversed an ether made up of tiny particles. As it moved on from one particle to the neighboring particle, the vibrations of the first particle spread to the second particle, those of the third to the fourth, and so on, in a kind of chain reaction. Light thus had a wavelike motion, behaving like water, whose surface if disturbed by a small thrust of the palm, would show waves, each created by its forerunner. Tiny waves of light in large numbers strengthening each other produced a wave-front, and the movement of this wave-front amounted to the radiation of light.

By means of geometry, Huygens demonstrated that such a wave-front could be (1) refracted, and, (2) reflected, in the same way as is a beam or ray of light. Moreover, should each point of a wave-front provide a center for little waves to produce a new wave-front, then light would pass only through a gap in a ray or beam, almost without spilling over into shadow. Theories were complicated by the old problem of the colors which appeared when light passed through transparent substances. During the Middle Ages scientists had observed that light was broken up into the colors of the rainbow by a prism, and they had struggled to explain this. Newton achieved his first notable feat in the world of physics when he succeeded at last in offering an explanation.

Elected a Fellow of the Royal Society in 1672, Newton soon afterward published his *New Theory about Light and Colors,* toward which he had for some years been working. Previously, he had given three short courses on optics at Cambridge in his position of Lucasian Professor of Mathematics. Meanwhile, he had also deposited with the Royal Society the reflecting telescope he had constructed to avoid chromatic aberration. Chromatic aberration is the tendency of light to break up into colors, which he thought — mistakenly as it later turned out — to be incurable.

In the 1670's, Newton was strenuously defending his theories about light, and his optical discoveries. He was attacked by Robert Hooke, and he was involved in controversy with Huygens, also. Scientists of the Middle Ages believed that when light showed up in the colors of the rainbow the blue light was most refracted, the red least. But they could not fathom whether light itself consisted of these colors or whether some characteristics of the transparent substance through which it passed was responsible for breaking it up and causing the rainbow effect. Newton's logic, directed by uncomplicated but effective experiment, penetrated the secret.

He used a prism of triangular glass, which offers the simplest kind of refraction. Working with a narrow light beam in a dark room, he caught the "rainbow" on a screen as clearly as he possibly could. The axis of the "rainbow" or *spectrum,* was at right angles to the prism and the spectrum was more or less rectangular in shape. What struck him and excited his curiosity was not only that the image was rectangular rather than round, but that it was some five times as long as it was broad. No matter how he positioned his equipment the same proportions obtained.

Newton checked results against the Sine Law of Snell and Descartes and satisfied himself that the spectrum was about as broad as it should be. But the angular length, and what the Sine Law said this should be, did not tally. Could the refractive rays be curved? Newton thought not because the length of the spectrum varied in proportion to its distance from the prism. Did the color rays proceed in different directions from their source? Could one ray be more emphatically bent than another?

He went on to what he himself described as his "crucial experiment" in order to find answers to these questions. Between two prisms he set a board with two holes in it. He directed a beam of light through the first prism and then through the holes in the board to keep the beam thin and exact. Finally he directed it through the second of his two prisms. The advantage was that he could select the color of the thin beam he wished to aim at the second of his prisms by juggling slightly the position of the first. Watching his screen, he noted that they differed according to the color of light he selected to aim at the second prism. Thus, he confirmed that the blue was refracted far more than the red.

Newton was confident he had proved that white light itself consists of colors, and that the colors do not result from a characteristic of the transparent substance through which the white light passes. "White light," he said, "is a confused aggregate of rays indued with all sorts of colors." Not only did each ray possess its own color, it possessed its own degree of refraction. The prism was the means of breaking up light into its colors: he told how he focused the colors by means of a big convex glass and found they merged into white light again.

Newton's view was contrary to that of Huygens who thought in terms of two-color light: yellow and blue. Newton pointed out that if white light consisted only of yellow and blue, a prism would break light up into just those two colors and the spectrum effect, which anybody with a prism could display, would never result. While investigating colors produced by oil on water, and by a thin layer of mica, he became aware of their "grainy" quality and guessed that both matter and light consisted of particles or atoms. Like Descartes, he visualized light as made up of particles, and rays of light as the course of these particles reflected. Hooke, on the other hand, visualized light as periodic motion, though he was inclined to agree with Descartes that colored light was a modified kind of white light. What he could not bring himself to believe was that since each color possessed not only its property of color, but its own degree of refraction, it could not just shed these features and mingle with others to make white light. Did the substance through which light passed have any effect upon the different refracting powers of the rays which caused dispersion? Both Hooke and Newton were inclined to think it did not.

About half a century later, it was to be shown that dispersion and refraction must be distinguished from each other, and that their relationship changed according to the kind of glass used.

Newton could not convince himself that light was transmitted in wave form, but preferred to think it traveled in straightlines. If light was transmitted in wave form, then it had to be capable of "bending" around obstacles as water "bends" around rocks. Newton found the idea difficult to accept. Yet Grimaldi thought that light rays were not always straight and that as they passed near some object they were "bent," or *diffracted.* Taking his cue from Grimaldi, Huygens explained diffraction as the result of wave motion, which would account also for the colors produced when light passed through thinly cut layers of a substance like mica.

Thus, the great scientists Newton and Huygens were in dispute. Their arguments brought to the forefront two principles set out by Fermat, and by his countryman, Pierre Louis de Maupertuis (1698–1759), who was head of Frederick the Great's Academy of Sciences in Berlin, a member of the Royal Society, London, and a supporter of Newton's Theory of Gravitation when the majority of French scholars were fighting against it with all their might because they preferred the ideas of Descartes. Nature, Fermat pointed out, operates in the most direct way. A wave, therefore, moved between two points in the shortest possible time. Maupertuis, for his part, pointed out that a particle did what it had to do with as little exertion as possible.

Thus, *minimum time* with waves and *minimum action* with particles, according to the principles enunciated by

Fermat and Maupertuis. Moreover, both waves and particles took the shortest possible cut. Was then every particle accompanied by a wave? Was every wave made up of particles arrayed in the form of a wave-front? In our own century, these important concepts led to modern wave mechanics.

Part Two: 6

NEWTON'S accomplishments in optics were impressive but his Theory of Gravitation was his most original contribution to human thought. It was the crowning point of intellectual trends that had been gathering strength since the days of Copernicus, Galileo, and Kepler, a triumph for Man's new-found ability to survey the heavens with his telescopes.

Kepler demonstrated that the planets followed an elliptical course around the sun. But what kept them on course? Why did they not shoot off erratically into space? And why were their orbits elliptical rather than circular? These questions were disputed by Edmund Halley, Newton's friend; Robert Hooke; and Christopher Wren (1632–1723), professor of astronomy at Oxford, who became the architect of St. Paul's Cathedral and several other beautiful London churches after the Great Fire of 1666. Hooke, a hunchback and an "irascible gnome," had a highly ingenious mind which led him to devise a number of valuable "gadgets" for science. He learned the experimental method from Robert Boyle (1627–91), who in 1662 gave us Boyle's Law (*the volume of a gas varies inversely with its pressure*), and was a founder of the Royal Society. Hooke lacked Boyle's drive and tenacity, was too ready a theorist, and could not approach Newton's extraordinary mathematical genius. Hooke's job as curator to the Royal Society suited him well because it asked for just the extensive scientific knowledge he possessed.

Halley has been described as by far the most gifted of English astronomers in those times. Perhaps he tried to exercise his gifts in too wide a field of learning, yet he has several notable feats to his credit. He excelled in mathematics and in theoretical astronomy, especially when he predicted the comet named after him. The idea of "attraction" had been very much in the air since 1600 when William Gilbert, physician to Queen Elizabeth I, had brought out a book on magnets. Sixty-six years later, the Italian Giovanni Alphonso Borelli (1608–79) realized that planetary motion meant that a centripetal, or gravitational, force had to exist in order to balance centrifugal force. Halley had much the same notion and spoke of the sun's "force of attraction," which he was convinced would operate when planetary orbits were circular. Would it operate when planetary orbits were elliptical? He was almost sure it would. He even offered a prize for the solution of this scientific conundrum. Observations, and mathematical support for those observations, were needed to frame an answer. But who could supply them? They did not know it, but Newton's qualifications perfectly met the bill.

Isaac Newton was the posthumous son of a small Lincolnshire farmer who belonged to the new rural middle class. Newton went to study at Cambridge University but did not have a particularly dazzling career. However, Isaac Barrow, Lucasian Professor of Mathematics there, was able to gauge the hidden potential of his twenty-one-year-old student. Barrow had Newton appointed to his own chair at the age of twenty-six. Oddly, Newton seems to have had little impact upon the university and never collected about him a group of followers. A good middle-of-the-roader in politics, and something of an idealist in outlook, he could hardly have been expected to be the author of a revolutionary hypothesis.

Newton was an odd fish. He was suspicious, secretive, and overly self-critical, which made him almost morbidly sensitive to the criticism of others. His tendency to retire into himself, and his other unfavorable characteristics were symptoms of a mental illness that began to manifest itself when he was about thirty. Often he got up very early in the morning and then sat perched on the edge of his bed for hour after hour, thinking. On one occasion a friend turned up at his invitation to dine with him. Time went by and Newton failed to appear, so the friend decided to eat the meal that was set out on the table. When Newton eventually came in he caught sight of the empty dishes. "Well, sir," he observed without great astonishment, "I thought I had not dined but I see I was wrong!" Toward the end of his life, his condition worsened, and because he imagined his friends and others were trying to persecute him, he hit back at them resentfully.

In 1665, Newton returned home to his native village of Woolsthorpe because of the plague, and while there he is said to have been awakened from a sleep by an apple falling on his head. Why, he pondered, did the apple fall down? Why did it not shoot up? We do not know whether the falling-apple story or some other version of it, is true or not. Nor can we accord him exclusive credit for his Theory of Gravitation. Others had contributed something toward it.

Exclusive credit goes to him for giving it mathematical expression. He transformed a physical picture into a mathematical one and thereby proved it to be true and open to verification by any observer. Observations in their turn yielded principles that were equally capable of verification. His conclusions enabled astronomers to plot far more exactly, and in far shorter time than before, the position of the moon and the planets. As another result, nautical tables were compiled that were far more precise than ever before. To add a flourish to such gains, Newton's friend, Halley, using the new methods, was able to forecast correctly the return of his comet.

To accomplish a truly stupendous feat, Newton employed the infinitesimal calculus, or, as he himself described it, "the method of fluxions." Calculus is a general name given to ways of calculating such matters as changing speeds, problems of flight, of electrical circuits, or of stresses set up in the framework of a bridge. It is (and here is the central point) an approach to the study of quantities that are continuously varying. It was first proposed by a Greek mathematician, Archimedes, in the third century B.C. and he used it for discovering the areas of curved figures and for drawing tangents to curves. Descartes and Fermat carried it much further and both Newton and the German scholar Gottfried Wilhelm Leibniz (1646–1716), worked it out in its modern form. The claims of Newton and Leibniz, the two contenders for the distinction of introducing the calculus, led to unpleasant quarrels. In his worst moments, Newton bitterly refuted Leibniz's claim and pursued a vendetta against him even after the German's death.

The irony was that Newton became obsessed with an issue of comparatively small importance. Who devised the infinitesimal calculus mattered far less than the incontestable fact that Newton was the one who applied it to answering questions of immeasurable importance to science.

We have an odd sidelight upon this issue when we consider the circumstances under which Newton came to publish his celebrated theory. As we have seen, Halley, Hooke, and Wren were convinced that the Law of Gravitation was true, but they required proof. Halley decided to consult Newton, the famous Cambridge professor of mathematics, and he went there to talk to him. The question Halley put was, "What would be the curve described by the planets supposing that the gravity diminished as the square of the distance?" Unhesitatingly Newton replied, "An ellipse." Halley was delighted to have his own views confirmed but he was astounded by Newton's unhesitating answer. "How do you know?" he immediately came back, to be informed by Newton, "Because I have already calculated it."

Naturally enough, Halley asked to see the calculations

but he hardly knew what to think when Newton confessed he had mislaid them. Was it credible that a man had mislaid the answer to a problem that had been taxing the most eminent minds of Europe? Halley was somewhat reassured when Newton promised to send along the calculations.

Returning to his work, Newton decided that it needed more done on it. To clear his own mind, as it were, he lectured on *The Motions of Bodies* during the Michaelmas term of 1684. Finally he sent Halley the material he had promised. Halley was understandably very excited, and any doubts he might have been nursing vanished. He hastened off to Cambridge again and urged Newton to present his work to the Royal Society. He had to use all his powers of persuasion and coaxed Newton to agree. Was a book to be entitled, as the lectures were, *The Motions of the Bodies?* After due consideration, the more impressive-sounding title chosen was *Philosophiae Naturalis Principia Mathematica (Mathematical Principles of Natural Philosophy).*

The first book was presented to the Royal Society in 1686. Since the Society was short of funds, publication was financed by Halley out of his own pocket. Newton and Hooke had been at loggerheads before and hostility between them flared up decisively now. Hooke believed that Newton had "borrowed" his ideas, worked out his thesis, and was preparing to hog the credit properly due to him. Their saddening dispute meant that Hooke to all intents and purposes gave up his activities at the Royal Society and that Newton himself resolved to give up his life at the university and, indeed, science itself.

The *Principia* of Newton has been described by Professor

J. D. Bernal as a work that "in sustained development of physical argument is unequalled in the whole history of science. Mathematically it can be compared only to Euclid's *Elements*; in its physical insights and its effect on ideas only to Darwin's *Origin of Species*. It immediately became the bible of the new science." But its influence was chiefly in England to begin with. It took almost half a century before Newton was acknowledged on the Continent, particularly in France, where his champions were de Maupertuis; Madame du Châtelet, a woman of scientific and mathematical learning; and her friend, the writer and philosopher Voltaire (1694–1778), "the greatest name in Europe." Huygens himself, Cassini, and Leibniz, curiously enough, thought Newton's hypothesis was unscientific and mystical. They clung to Descartes whose views — equally curiously — struck them as unassailably rational.

In the end Newton became the sole master of European science. It is a revealing comment upon our civilization that he was knighted not for the one feat of his life that counted but for the rather commonplace services he rendered to politics. In his synthesis, he dispelled chaos and showed how the universe was ordered by a simple law. He expounded his Universal Law of Gravitation in this way:

> Every particle of matter in the universe attracts every other particle with a force whose direction is that of a line joining the two, and whose magnitude is directly as the product of the two masses, and inversely as the square of their distance from each other.

The *Principia* is far from easy and Newton realized that

it needed to be as clear as he could possibly make it. He therefore put the whole thing into the terms of Greek geometry so that it would be more accessible both to mathematicians and to astronomers. Even so, his ideas were spread about not so much by his own book as by various popularizations of it that enabled far more people to grasp its momentous implications, including scholars of repute who had been baffled by the original.

Volumes have been written in an attempt to deduce what effect Newton's thought had on the world. Everybody agrees that the effect was enormous but few agree about what it was. Two important aspects, however, attract our attention. First, Newton did not for one moment visualize the laws of nature in the cloudy terms of religion. He visualized them as capable of revelation and explanation by sound mathematical logic. To him, philosophy meant the investigation of nature's forces in terms of motion. From these forces, he thought, other phenomena could be demonstrated. Nothing was the product of chance, nothing took place for some arbitrary reason. Natural events, however far removed from each other and however disconnected they might seem, were, in truth, connected. It was for us to penetrate their interrelationships, which depended upon a few basic rules. Were these rules "built into" nature? Newton hesitated. He could not bring himself to avow a materialistic theory. Instead, he adopted a compromise which in his day was common enough. Even Voltaire, that arch-enemy of the Church, subscribed to it.

Here was the universe; somewhere there had to be an Architect of the universe. God had created the universe and had set it spinning. He and His angels saw to it that there was no running down. Newton's theory reduced somewhat this old proposition. True, God had set the universe in motion but it would keep going without divine aid because of the laws under which God had in the first place established its motion. Such compromises fitted well the social and political climate of the day in which the absolute power of the Church and that of monarchs had been undermined. In England, the Stuarts with their claims to rule by "divine right" had been dismissed from the throne by the English Revolution of 1688. The fixed order was passing, and Newton in his hypothesis expressed preference for the dynamic over the static. Moreover, the Reformation and the rise of Protestantism encouraged men to believe that each individual could create his own relationship to God and approach the Almighty by praying directly to Him. No longer was the Church the only mediator.

Leeuwenhoek Explores a World Once Unseen

Part Three: I

NEWTON'S majestic work, in a sense, crowned the chain of events begun by the discoverers of optic glasses in Holland, who contrived to be more than the spectacle makers they proclaimed they were. They roamed from city to city, ostensibly to sell their wares but often to carry intelligence, for many of them were serving the Resistance to the Spanish occupiers of their homeland. Often they spread false coinage to weaken the strength of Spanish currency in Holland. Their legitimate work gave us both telescope and microscope, which, to begin with, was the short-focus telescope.

In 1592, Georg Hofnagel (1545–1600), probably assisted by his son, published, at Frankfurt, Germany, a book illustrating a number of natural objects. Its drawings contain so much detail that we can be reasonably sure he used a magnifying glass to study what he pictured. Indeed, many authorities regard Hofnagel's as the first work to record objects viewed under some form of magnification. Similarly, Christoph Scheiner, and Francesco Stelluti (1577–1653), employed the microscope to produce wonderfully delicate drawings of insect anatomy. Athanasius Kircher (1661–80), like Scheiner a Jesuit priest, darkly sighted what he chose to describe as "little worms." It seems unlikely that he ever caught a glimpse of any microrganism, but his *Ars Magna Lucis et Umbrae*, published at Rome in 1646, conveys to us how he (and, indeed, others also) strained to penetrate the barriers between the visible and invisible worlds. They sensed the invisible world to be both inside and outside the living things with which we are all familiar. Kircher listed six kinds of microscopes available in his day, including spheres and hemispheres of glass filled with water and a simple microscope with two convex lenses.

The microscope, so named in 1625, was not really used for scientific research until a quarter of a century later, although one writer described it as, "for those who wish to study the majesty of God in minute creation." People were not entirely satisfied with an instrument that permitted inspection through one eye only and sometime before 1610 two similar instruments were ranged alongside each other at the average distance between the eyes. We have an illustration of such a binocular microscope constructed by a Frenchman, Cherubin Orleans, in 1677. It is the prototype of our own binocular, or opera glass.

By about 1650, the compound microscope usually had biconvex eye lens and objective, with a planoconvex field lens set between the two in order to concentrate the light rays. Hooke mounted one of his instruments so that it could be tilted to any angle desired by the operator. He used a small oil lamp to brighten opaque objects. Often the apparatus had an opening in the base to admit light from a candle on the floor, which illuminated transparent objects. There were various means of adjusting microscopes, but Hevelius bettered most existing devices with his screw-and-slide method.

Although compound microscopes could easily enough be handled, scientists often preferred simple microscopes which were as easy, if not easier, to manipulate. If of low power they gave more reliable results. The optical qualities of compound microscopes left a great deal to be desired. The object, when too greatly magnified, became ill-defined and detail was easily lost. Manufacturers of microscopes and telescopes, often one and the same person or firm, complained that not enough craftsmen with the skills required for their kind of work were available. They also shared the problem of securing stable fittings to spare users inconvenience. Edmund Culpepper (1601–1738) ultimately achieved stability by using a tripod, but the old pillar-fitting continued to be popular for almost two centuries. Indeed, stable fittings were not really devised until the beginning of the nineteenth century.

But, whatever the external defects, the grinding of good lenses remained always the heart of the matter. Technicians cast about for ways and means of improvement. They sought inspiration in mechanical principals depicted by Leonardo da Vinci for the working of metallic mirrors. Painter, sculptor, architect, musician, and scientist, there seemed hardly anything else the extraordinary Leonardo could be. No wonder he has been described by one of his biographers as "unique among all the men of history because he distinguished himself in so many fields of human activity." From the fertile mind of Huygens, sprang the notion of using a lever for a pivot to which he attached the glass blank. A weight moving along an arm helped the operator to apply force to the grinding tool. Newton himself proposed designs for lens-grinding apparatus, and Hevelius, with swifter production in mind, put forward a method of grinding a number of small lenses at one and the same time. Always, scientists and technicians kept playing with the possibilities of the machine. What if the glass blank, or the tool, or, for that matter, both, could be kept mechanically spinning? But the problem was that machinery cranked by handle, or driven by wheel and belt, or by gears, generally called for two operators and did not offer the precision demanded in lens grinding, especially in the delicate final stages.

Polishing represented the last, most refined phase in the whole process. Polishing shaped the glass exactly and brought it up smooth and shining in order to ensure the best possible visibility through it. Machines and instruments might do up to that point but, in the end, it became a labor of the hands, until buffing was carried out on a treadle-operated lathe.

We are quite accustomed to the idea of machines, under the direction of men, achieving almost incredible feats of precision. We therefore have to make a real effort to transport ourselves through some three centuries to a time when the skill of the human manipulator was almost everything. One man who personifies for us all this skill was the Dutchman Antony van Leeuwenhoek (1632–1723), who turned himself into a master grinder of lenses and made wonderfully simple but effective microscopes. His lenses have been praised as "the finest of Newton's age." They could magnify up to 400 times, though at such magnification no specimen would show up clearly. Proper definition could be obtained only at the sacrifice of magnifying power. Nevertheless, van Leeuwenhoek described objects as small as 1/10,000 inch across. Some of his observations were so keen they were not repeated until a hundred or more years after his death by microscopists who had at their disposal instruments in which chromatic aberration had largely been overcome.

Van Leeuwenhoek had to combat the defects of the compound microscope with its three- or four-lens system, which, as we have said, denied scientists very high powers of magnification because at very high power, the image grew too blurred for detailed inspection. On the other hand, little biconvex lenses of short focal length were needed for objectives in the compound equipment, and craftsmen had the complicated and taxing job of producing them. Van Leeuwenhoek appreciated that these little, high-power lenses gave exceptionally good results when mounted as simple microscopes, but to obtain such results a lens had to be no more than 1/10 inch in diameter and, if possible, even less. Many makers were deterred by the hardships involved in their manufacture, but to van Leeuwenhoek the challenge proved irresistible. Even the appalling strain on the eyes did not put him off. He did not always manage to grind lenses of outstanding quality but at least one that has come down to us was tested and declared to be "far superior to any other known simple lens." Unfortunately, only a few of his instruments have survived. One example is to be seen at the museum of the University of Leyden in Holland.

Van Leeuwenhoek was a very ordinary fellow who did some very extraordinary things. His father was a basket maker and his mother the daughter of a brewer. Born in Delft he spent the whole of his adult life there, although he did pay a visit to London in 1680. He had some training as a land surveyor but he was by trade a draper, and in addition to running a drapery store, he was chamberlain to the sheriffs of Delft and the city's official wine gauger.

However, all these activities he took in his stride; they were in the day's work. His precious microscopes were, in sharp contrast, different; they evoked his utmost dedication. With them he spent every one of his worthwhile hours. Van Leeuwenhoek was the forerunner of the modern specialist who concentrates upon a single narrow corner of science, which he cultivates intensively. He gave the impression of a rather dry stick, inclined to be crusty and suspicious. He trusted no one with his beloved microscopes and when a prince once visited him to inspect his celebrated collection he never left the room, in order constantly to keep them under supervision. Moreover, when he had to step out for a moment to comply with some royal request, he carried his instruments away with him, bringing them back when he returned. He was certainly not prepared to put his trust even in princes.

Van Leeuwenhoek was a superb technician. Was he also a scientist in the more generous sense of that word? Some historians of science have viewed him as an oddity because he was a lone explorer of that "world of the infinitely small" which Pasteur was so dramatically to exhibit about a century and a half later. His fellow-scientists did not trouble much about microorganisms; they were content to explore with their microscopes the surfaces of plants and animals. Thus van Leeuwenhoek was a pioneer microbiologist. As we, after all these years, contemplate him immersed in his labors, the dry man recedes and we catch a hint of passion as he peers through his lenses at various bacteria and lovingly croons over them, his "little animals."

Just what were his "little animals?"

In those days, the scientists of different countries exchanged information about their researches by writing somewhat formal letters to each other. A Frenchman who received a document from a Dutch or an English colleague might then have had it published in a learned journal, often one issued by his Academy. On the other hand a scientist, no matter what his nationality, might decide to communicate directly with a foreign academy. The Royal Society in London thus received from foreign scientists many such communications, which were included in its *Philosophical Transactions*. Van Leeuwenhoek wrote directly to the Royal Society. Since he knew no language other than his own, his reports were in Dutch and had to be translated into English.

His lack of education handicapped him even more seriously for he was able to read the works of Dutch scholars only. Yet this drawback in one sense proved to be an advantage because he was not carried away by the main trends of international research, but confined himself to his own inimitable observations. It was not his fault that he was unable to relate the microorganisms he sighted to the whole great scheme of life, or detect in them the cause of many diseases.

Nobody at that time had any idea that living things could consist of one single cell, or millions and millions of cells as we ourselves do. Indeed, not until 1839, did two German scientists, Matthias Jakob Schleiden (1801–84) and Theodor Schwann (1810–82), teach that life in all its forms is made up of cells. Van Leeuwenhoek's letters to the Royal Society may nowadays strike us as simple because he wrote in his natural, unstyled language. Nevertheless, they tell us vividly and accurately just what he saw. He does not theorize and, again, while this is a strength, it is also a weakness for he offers us no general theory based on his observations.

In a letter to the Royal Society dated March 23, 1677, he recounts how he saw "little animals" in a drop of water and how he worked out their numbers. He begins by expressing no surprise that "the Philosophers" (scientists were in those days, and are still, "seekers after wisdom") could not credit his observations of thousands of "little animals" in a drop of water. "I can't wonder at it," he goes on, "since it's hard to understand such matters without getting a sight of them." He then tells of the method he used to count his microbes:

This amount of water, as big as a millet-seed, I introduce into a clean little glass tube (whenever I wish to let some curious person or other look at it). This slender little glass tube, containing the water, I divide again into 25 or 30, or more, parts; and I then bring it before my microscope by means of two silver or copper springs which I have attached to it for the purpose, so as to be able to place the little glass tube before my microscope in any position I desire, and to be able to push it up or down as I think fit.

He showed his drop of water to a certain gentleman who gave his own opinion about the numbers of "little animals" he noticed. "Now supposing," says van Leeuwenhoek, "that this gentleman really saw 1,000 animalcules in a particle of water but 1/30,000 of the bigness of a millet-seed, and consequently 2,730,000 living creatures in one drop of water . . ."

The idea he planted in scientists' minds was of an invisible world, existing in unimaginable profusion alongside the visible world, which had hitherto seemed to be the only one. Thus, he introduced two worlds where before there had only been one. Accordingly, the microscope aroused Man's consciousness of small, near things just as the telescope aroused his consciousness of the distant.

Not unexpectedly, the thrill of new horizons led to wild speculations. Parallels with the workings of things more familiar were easily but unwisely drawn to explain new discoveries and led inevitably to mistaken conclusions. Both the heavenly bodies twinkling brightly in outer space, and microorganisms wriggling in a drop of water had to be explained by their own rules yet to be disclosed.

Part Three: 2

VAN LEEUWENHOEK'S endeavors may have lain outside the mainstream of biology, yet he contributed to many keen arguments of the day. It was then imagined that life could begin spontaneously: that living things could be born of "decaying matter," without parents. The error had sprung up with the ancients because people had not correctly related cause and effect. They had noticed fleas hopping in sand and concluded that they were born of the sand. Likewise, they had noticed weevils in grain storehouses and concluded that they were born of the grain.

Exploring such matters with his microscopes and his characteristic persistence, van Leeuwenhoek was inclined to oppose the theory of Spontaneous Generation. He observed the lives and habits of fleas well enough to write a remarkable account of those insects, but struck no evidence whatever to convince him they were born of sand. His objections to Spontaneous Generation hardened after he had studied thoroughly the lives and habits of weevils. Far from being born of grain, they were just grubs hatched out of eggs deposited by winged insects.

The theory of Spontaneous Generation continued to be held obstinately against demonstrations of its improbability not only by van Leeuwenhoek, but by Francesco Redi (1626–97), a doctor of Arezzo in Italy, and by a fiery and original Jesuit, Lazarro Spallanzani (1729–99), of Modena, who disputed the question vehemently with an Englishman long resident in Paris, J. T. Needham, thereby dividing both scientists and intelligentsia of Europe into two hostile camps. Redi showed that maggots appeared in meat only when it was exposed because they were hatched from eggs laid by flies. When he kept the flies off by covering the meat with gauze no maggots appeared. Spallanzani boiled his materials in a flask corked up tightly enough to exclude air. They remained uncontaminated, which they did not if exposed to the air. However, there are certain kinds of bacteria that, in spore form particularly, can resist great extremes of heat and cold, and Spallanzani, although unaware of their existence, went on to distinguish between a "higher order of animalcules" which succumb more easily to heat than do a "lower order."

Spontaneous Generation embarrassed the progress of science until Pasteur, after vivid contests with its staunch upholders, finally disposed of the theory in the 1860's.

The key to an understanding of events during the seventeenth century is to be found in the new comprehension of the universe as a marvelous piece of machinery. "Celestial machinery" is a phrase that recurs constantly in writings of the times. Using no more than a magnifying glass, the Englishman William Harvey (1578–1657) watched the beating hearts of living creatures, particularly insects; he did his dissections carefully and, by 1615, had a very clear idea of how the heart pumped blood through the body. But not until 1628, did he publish a short book, *De Moto Cordis* (*The Movement of the Heart*), which revolutionized physiology and has been described as one of the greatest works ever written in the medical field.

Significantly he saw the heart at the center of the body, like the sun at the "heart of the World," and he saw it, too, as the center of a mechanical system, a pump that spread blood throughout the body in a perfectly logical manner, continuously, and invariably in the same direction.

Although he was convinced that blood is carried from the arteries to the veins by means of small capillary vessels, he could not demonstrate it without a microscope. Employing the microscope, however, both van Leeuwenhoek, and the Italian Marcello Malpighi (1628–94) were able to furnish the proof that, under the circumstances, was bound to elude Harvey. It is of more than passing interest that van Leeuwenhoek also described the red corpuscles of the blood. Indeed, van Leeuwenhoek, who liked to make instruments suitable to the objects he proposed to study, adapted a microscope for the sole purpose of investigating the blood circulation in the tail of a young eel. Using extraordinary powers of near vision he worked out the dimensions of its red corpuscles and drew them for us; he drew also the capillaries joining arteries and veins, both in the eel and in the frog.

Van Leeuwenhoek was actually preceded in such researches by Malpighi who in 1661 wrote to his friend Giovanni Alfonso Borelli (1608–79), an eminent mathematician, describing how he was able to fill in the missing part of Harvey's splendid thesis on the circulation of the blood. Fortunately, he chose for his investigation the lung of a frog which is practically transparent and in which the capillaries lie almost on the surface. He noted the same system of capillaries when he examined its distended urinary bladder. His successes came to the attention of the Royal Society which thereupon began to publish his accounts of the work he was carrying out in this and various other directions.

What most interested Malpighi was the structure of living things and he employed the microscope to try to penetrate their surfaces. He hoped plants might reveal more to his eyes because they were "simpler," but the structure of plants, as we now know, is in its way quite as complicated as that of "simple" animals. Malpighi was himself to demonstrate in a treatise on the silkworm that this lowly animal has a complex internal anatomy of its own with an organ to perform each separate function. However, straining to draw parallels between plants and animals often led to mistakes. When he looked at the gray matter of the brain he thought it was a glandular structure containing "vital spirit," a concept going back to Aristotle (384–322 B.C.), whose extended influence over scientific thought proved in the long run to be of disadvantage.

Aristotle believed that the distinction between living and nonliving things lay in the possession by living things of a *psyche* — a "vital spirit" or "force," which we ourselves refer to as "soul." Nowadays few scientists view the "soul" as their subject of inquiry, for so abstract a concept hardly falls within their purview. Moreover, Pasteur, during the second half of the nineteenth century, introduced an entirely novel slant into vitalism by showing that fermentation was a process for which living microorganisms were responsible. And we have, since Pasteur's day, carried such investigations a good deal further through the new departments of science which deal with bacteria (bacteriology), with viruses (virology), and with the minute internal contents of the cell (molecular biology).

Malpighi studied the embryo of the chicken within the first hour or two of its incubation and was misled into visualizing the fetus as "preformed." Thus, as in some prefabricated structure of modern days, the parts, already made, had simply to be "put together." Development of the fetus to him meant unfolding and growth of what was there from the very start. Van Leeuwenhoek, who had been first to sight the male spermatozoon naturally enough emphasized its importance in reproduction. To him the mother simply received the male germ and nourished it in her womb until it grew into a little human ready to take its place in the world.

We need not here embark upon the story of how, slowly and painfully, scientists came to discover, largely in our own century, that conception takes place when male spermatozoon and female egg fuse. The male spermatozoon normally bears twenty-three chromosomes and the female egg also normally bears twenty-three, so both parents are equal contributors. Thus, the new life starts as a cell with forty-six chromosomes, the sum total of its heredity. Development continues by a ceaseless process of cell division, which determines the formation of the many parts that make up the whole as a recognizable member of the human species.

A third great microscopist of the early years was another Dutchman, Jan Swammerdam (1637–80), who concentrated his attention on insects. His father was an apothecary and a naturalist of Amsterdam who kept a museum of curiosities. He began by helping his father in the museum but decided to become a doctor and qualified at the University of Leyden in 1667. While he pursued his medical studies he became wholly absorbed in the delicacies of insect dissection and lost interest in his doctoring. His life was made wretched through ill health (he was subject to malaria), and through mental instability, which led to quarrels, especially with his father (who ultimately disinherited him). He had a form of religious mania that made him almost unendurable even to those nearest and dearest to him. Yet none of these drawbacks affected his skill as a microscopist. He had a marvelously light touch and was adept at dissections calling for scrupulous technique. He was, indeed, the master technician of his time and introduced various injections which he prepared with great ingenuity in order to ensure the perfection of his work.

In 1672, the Dutch anatomist Regnier de Graaf announced that he had noticed the eggs of mammals. Working without a microscope, he had in reality seen only the follicle, or sac, containing the mammal's egg (ovum), which, about 1/10 inch in diameter, was not properly observed until 1827 by the German-Estonian scientist Karl von Baer. Swammerdam, at about the same time as de Graaf, was able to describe the ovarian follicle. He found out, too, that the snail was a hermaphrodite, containing in itself both male and female sexual organs, and that the queen bee possessed ovaries or egg-producing organs. He had observed diligently the growth of insects from the larval stage and maintained that no true transformation occurred when the caterpillar turned into a butterfly. He maintained that the same applied when a tadpole turned into a frog. Swammerdam's books embody for us the essence of his remarkable talents. His first, *A General History of Insects,* (1669), contains his own illustrations of those refined dissections he carried out. In 1675, he issued his *The Life-history of the Mayfly,* a full and rich account of the anatomy of that insect. This volume attracted attention in Paris and drew an offer designed to tempt him away to Florence. He did not accept.

At his death, Swammerdam left a mass of unpublished writings and drawings that Hermann Boerhaave (1668–1738) bought up and paid to have published. Boerhaave, a celebrated instructor in medicine at Leyden, and a widely cultivated man, was thus responsible for the salvation of Swammerdam's works, especially his priceless *Bible of Nature.*

Last, but not by any means least, among scientists who

tried to exploit the possibilities of the new microscope was the Englishman Robert Hooke, who remains a subject of controversy among the historians of science. Hooke's unfortunate personality, his wrath over the success of Newton at his expense (as he thought), and our own boundless admiration for Newton's achievement, doubtless affect our judgment of Hooke. Son of a poor clergyman from the Isle of Wight, Hooke managed to secure a place at Oriel College, Oxford. Robert Boyle happened to be at Oxford about the same time and Hooke sought him out as friend and mentor. Professor Bernal believes that he probably devised the apparatus for Boyle's experiments on vacuums and gases and even carried them out for him. He adds that Boyle performed no notable experiments after Hooke left him.

Ill health, and Hooke's own unfortunate appearance, probably accounted for his testy ways and his hypersensitivity, which at times amounted to a sense of persecution. He was the indefatigable servant of science in his position at the Royal Society, and Dr. Bernal considers him the greatest experimental physicist before Michael Faraday (1791–1867) who made so many epoch-making discoveries in electromagnetics. Hooke's inventions include the double-barreled air pump, the spirit level, the marine barometer, the sea gauge, the micrometer and the balance wheel, which helped to ensure accurate timekeeping. There are some who claim that he was also the originator of the inverse-square law and the notion of universal gravity. But, as we have mentioned, lacking Newton's mathematical genius, he was unable to give his deductions true voice.

In 1663, the Royal Society asked him to pursue his microscopical investigations, with their publication in view. He was then asked to prepare at least one topic on which to address each meeting of the society. His first presentation dealt with common moss and, we are told, delighted his listeners. Later he showed plant cells in the structure of cork. Although he was first to mention the word *cell* we cannot truly credit him with the discovery of the cell as we nowadays understand it. Malpighi referred to "chambers" in vegetable life but, again, we cannot really say that he meant by "chambers" what we mean by cells. Nevertheless, Hooke deserves praise for suggesting that the surface unity of living things concealed secrets of structure that the microscope was able to uncover.

In 1665, commanded to assemble a handsome volume for royalty, Hooke published his *Micrographia,* which he dedicated to Charles II and which bore the imprimatur of Lord Brouncker, President of the Royal Society. *Micrographia* was, of course, based on his previous offerings to the Society. On January 22, 1665, the diarist Pepys informs us he went around to his bookseller "and there took home Hooke's book of microscopy, a most excellent piece, and of which I am very proud." Proud he might well have been for Hooke's text was adorned by plates that Sir Christopher Wren had prepared. *Micrographia* is distinguished as the first book in English that was entirely devoted to the fruits of microscopical research.

Critics have complained that a fair proportion of Hooke's volume deals with neither microscopy nor biology, and that much of the biology is commonplace. They add that Hooke's description of an intricate type of compound microscope with various gadgets to assist the operator does not significantly augment its importance. At the end, Hooke is left muttering plaintively that devotees of the microscope are reduced to a single votary: van Leeuwenhoek.

The flea was in those days a popular object for observation under the microscope and Hooke records in *Micrographia* what he saw when he looked at one:

> The strength and beauty of this small creature, had it no other relation to Man, would deserve a description. For its strength the Microscope is able to make no greater discoveries of it than the naked eye, but only the curious contrivance of its legs and joints, for the exerting that strength, is very plainly manifested such as no other creature I have yet observed, has anything like it. . . . As for the beauty of it the Microscope manifests it to be all over adorned with a curiously polished suit of sable armor, neatly jointed, and beset with multitudes of sharp pins, shaped almost like porcupine's quills, or bright conical steel bodkins. . . .

The passage illustrates, perhaps, why Hooke has been regarded in some quarters as superficial. But, even if he appears to be overconcerned with the beauties of the flea, rather than with more profound considerations, he explains why: "For its strength the Microscope is able to make no greater discoveries of it than the naked eye." It is the admission of a man in the grip of the technical limitations of his apparatus and these, as we know, were not to be overcome until the nineteenth century.

Hooke himself made some contributions to the improvement of the instrument and he tells us how he regards light as "a very short vibrative motion transverse to the straight line of propagation through a homogeneous medium." He also includes accounts of his machines for lens grinding, and for measuring refractive indices. It was this measuring apparatus that enabled him to verify Snell's Law "with great accuracy." Whatever its quality, Hooke's compilation made a great hit, not only in England, but abroad.

Hooke's work characterizes, perhaps, much that was done in his day. Delighted with the new tool in their hands, scientists excitedly put it to every sort of enterprise they could think of. The extensive use they made of the microscope, no doubt, kept them from delving in one single direction, and earned for them the accusation of superficiality. They were trying, too, always to tax the microscope beyond the limits it imposed upon them. Such expansiveness of approach may be the reason why the biological and medical implications of van Leeuwenhoek's early investigations of the invisible world of microorganisms remained unpursued.

Suddenly the telescope and the microscope provided men with a new mental dimension. They could see farther; they could see deeper. Of what are insects and animals made? How do they work? Of what are plants made? How do they work? And what differences mark the workings of the animal and vegetable kingdoms? Scholars did not always ask the right questions, or they asked questions that were too big for easy answers. They tended still to think in terms of those "august abstractions," those "grandiose generalizations," which distinguished the ancient way of regarding the "mysteries," of existence. Thus, scientists of the time were most successful when they could employ the discipline of mathematics as a tool with which to bring their ideas to fruition. Galileo, Descartes, and Newton were, first and foremost, mathematicians.

The most important consequences of telescope and microscope really lay ahead, but already nature was being opposed to supernature. The old "magical" picture of the universe, of our earth, of Man and the other living things upon it, was for the first time challenged by the new "realities" of science. No matter how meager the revelations to the eye of microscope and telescope (and they were not really meager), they signaled the beginnings of a "scientific attitude" that has, since that time, been drawing us inexorably closer to "reality" as tested by experiment, and farther and farther away from the one-time "magic" grounded in "revelations" of religion, which, unlike the "new" revelations of science, could not be investigated under the microscope or drawn into view by a telescope.

It is ironic, that those who made possible this intellectual revolution proclaimed their faithfulness to the old beliefs. Newton, for example, devoted much of his time and energy to the contemplation of religious topics; so did Swammerdam. Perhaps it is only in retrospect that we can discern the first thrusts by science against the well-formed and well-hardened crusts of a passing world that was, in passing, to take with it many of its articles of faith.

Astrology Yields to Science

Part Four: I

NEWTON, it has been said, was not the first of the new prophets, but the last of a line of "old magicians" stretching back to the most ancient civilizations. Certainly after his death, and the death of Cassini, the spectacular triumphs of astronomy that the invention of the telescope had stimulated declined. The less spectacular accomplishments of the biologists also hit a plateau. We can, to some extent, account for this unproductive period by recollecting that neither telescope nor microscope were decisively improved until the middle of the eighteenth century, and after climbing stupendous heights, there had to be a "plateau of rest." After the "grand declarations," the great theories, came the time of practical applications. Seamen were opening up the world and overseas trade was flourishing. Astronomers turned to the problems of navigation and surveying. Positional astronomy became their concern.

We owe to mathematicians the restoration of astronomy to something like its old grandeur. The brothers Bernouilli, and Leonhard Euler, all Swiss, and others, laid the groundwork for four great Frenchmen: Alexis Clairaut (1713–65), a prodigy who lived hard and died relatively young; Jean d'Alembert (1714–83), the illegitimate son of a Parisian hostess who abandoned him on the steps of a church, from where he was rescued by the wife of a poor glazier; Joseph Louis Lagrange (1736–1813), honored most by those who least understood him, like Louis XVI, Frederick II and Napoleon himself; and, finally, Pierre Simon Laplace (1749–1827), son of a prosperous Norman farmer who came to be known as the "French Newton" and was the recipient of innumerable honors that those in high places showered upon him. His *Mécanique Céleste* (*Celestial Mechanics*) was in its way as original and as influential as Newton's *Principia* had been, or as the works of Darwin and Pasteur were to be.

It was once again about "celestial mechanics," but with a sharply different approach. Rationalism by now outweighed the "magical" in science. God had "set off" the universe. Did he also have every now and then to keep it going with a push? The question to us nowadays sounds absurd, but it was being asked in deadly earnest not all that many years ago. Some feared that if God did not give planets the occasional push necessary they would slow down to such an extent that they would all be "sucked in" disastrously by the sun. Even Newton had wondered whether our system needed that divine push because some of its erratic workings appeared to hint at the possibility of future breakdown. Laplace was able to explain that these erratic workings of the planets were self-adjusting. A little to one way was, in time, put right by a little to the other.

The stability of our universe was, therefore, not in doubt, and it was to proceed indefinitely. No divine push at intervals to keep it going was required, nor was its collapse to be feared. In 1759, Clairaut had forecast with perfect accuracy the return of Halley's comet, demonstrating thereby the potency of the new "magic" of science. Laplace's reassurances, which came toward the end of the eighteenth century, (1798–99) seemed to underline that potency.

But somebody, somewhere, had to pick up a telescope again and try to repeat the feats of Galileo and the early pioneers; it could not all be left to the mathematicians. The man for the occasion was, like the great composer Handel, a German who had reached England after the House of Hanover had been settled on the English throne (1714). His name was William Herschel (1738–1822), son of a gardener who had imparted to his son some of his musical gifts. William Herschel went to live at Bath, a west of England spa, where he managed to subsist on his small earnings as organist, music teacher, and occasional concert performer. Astronomy was his escape from the hard grind of the day and from the depressing contemplation of his unpromising prospects. He spent his nights reading books about astronomy. Having amassed some knowledge of the subject, he realized that there never could be any question of turning astronomer merely by reading. The telescope was the real astronomer's tool of trade and he had to have one. But telescopes were costly and Herschel had no money. He decided there was nothing for it but to make one. In order to do so, he transformed his kitchen into a foundry and his sitting room into an optical workshop.

Refracting telescopes with their long tubes were hardly suitable to the amateur without an observatory. The reflecting telescope was in every way more convenient though it, too, had its disadvantages. The operator using the reflecting telescope catches his image from the heavens with a concave mirror, not an object glass as with a refracting telescope. The mirror enlarges, but other arrangements for further increasing enlargement are also possible, after which the operator can examine his celestial body by means of a lens which serves as eye piece. Herschel appreciated, also, that he had to prepare only one surface of the mirror, but two surfaces of an object glass. He thus saved himself labor. The mirror was made not of glass, but of "white" bronze, which was easy to polish and did not readily tarnish. Moreover, such mirrors could be produced far bigger than the 4-inch object glasses usual in the refracting telescope. James Short (1710–68) had attained very high skill in the art of polishing large mirrors, and by exploiting the techniques employed in figuring and polishing, he had been able to parabolize the speculum, or metal mirror, used in telescopes. Helped no doubt by Short's successes Herschel in due course constructed a 48-inch mirror.

On March 4, 1774, Herschel was peering through his homemade reflecting instrument when he caught sight of the nebula of Orion. This was exciting, but even more excitement awaited him. On March 13, 1781, he noted a star in Gemini that exceeded all others in size. He could not place it. Since there was no record of its existence, he asked for guidance from the director of Greenwich Observatory. Herschel had, of course, sighted the planet Uranus and his discovery pushed out the frontiers of space in a way that astounded his contemporaries. Until that moment Saturn had been the farthest known planet from the sun. Uranus was about twice as far from the sun. What was more, Newton's law clearly operated even at this huge distance.

Induced by a promise, from George III, of monies that would enable him to pursue his hobby as a profession, the forty-four-year-old Herschel left Bath for Slough near Windsor, which he had picked as a site favorable for astronomical observations. The passerby was mystified by tubes and platforms and pulleys, by the sound of a man giving orders to other men as they cranked away at handles. His telescopes could now magnify perhaps 3,000, or 4,000, or even 5,000 times; they were equipped with giant reflectors that opened wider the heavens. The skies teemed with stars, as though some sower had passed by throwing them out by handfuls in order to leave no patch bare. There was our solar system: the sun with the planets moving round it. There were also these stars. Together, they formed the mighty universe. How were they related — if indeed they were related? What did it all mean?

In one sense, the astronomer is a man who sits and stares. So is the bacteriologist who gazes endlessly — so it seems — through the lenses of his microscope. From last light to first, both winter and summer, Herschel, on a little platform, stared up at the skies, breaking his silent vigil to instruct an assistant working the machinery of the telescope or to say some words to his sister Caroline, who sat at a little desk by her brother's feet recording his observations. He had no more loyal ally than his sister, who had lent him all her support since the poor days in Bath. Like her brother she was a musician turned self-taught astronomer who had learned as she went along. Often the iciest winter nights are the fittest for scanning the heavens, and brother and sister sat out through many, many of those. Once in the Bath days, she had, like a mother bird, dropped food into her brother's mouth because he dared not take his hands off the mirrors he was making. Now she rubbed warmth into him so that he could continue with his work, and into herself so that her fingers would be pliable enough to control the pen taking down what he told her he saw.

Were these stars they were observing fixed? Or did they move? He saw star pairs, with one star moving around the other. Was it the force of gravity that kept them together? He thought it had to be, so he calculated by Kepler's Laws how long the satellite would take to go around the "parent." For Castor, he found, it was 342 years. The important thing was that Kepler's laws, like Newton's applied equally to these far-off stars as they did to our own planets. Obviously, the most striking conclusion was that a few simple laws might apply throughout the whole mighty world of space.

Stars moved around each other. Did they also move about in space? An Alsatian tailor's apprentice, Johann Lambert (1728–77), thought they did. But the sun was also a star and it had long been regarded as fixed. Yet if it was a star and other stars moved about in space, why not the sun also? Herschel believed that if our solar system, as such, traveled across the heavens, then the stars that were not a part of it ought to be — so to speak — "left behind" us, speeding "away to the rear," for would we and they not be moving in opposite directions? He knew the direction of certain stars like Castor and Pollux and, beginning with this information, he got an answer in 1783. Observations convinced him that the solar system was moving toward an apex in the constellation Hercules. Indeed, it had been heading toward this apex since the unbelievable celestial universe had come into being at some time in the remote past. Moreover, the path of the solar system toward the point in Hercules was, as he suspected, in a direction exactly opposite to the one followed by the stars outside it.

Almost every book on astronomy these days bears on its cover, or contains within it, a picture of a nebula. Science fiction has celebrated among others that of Andromeda and the Triffid nebula in Sagittarius. As far back as 1610, Nicolas Fabri Pieresc (1580–1637), a counselor of the Aix Parliament in southern France, sighted the nebula of Orion. Two years later, Simon Marius or Mayer (1570–1623) spotted the great nebula of Andromeda. But the Frenchman Charles Messier (1730–1817), at his laboratory in Paris, had, by 1781, counted and listed some 300 nebulae. He claimed the discovery of sixty-one himself. We pay him tribute by adding the prefix M (for Messier's Catalogue) to the number of a nebula. Thus Andromeda is M 31 and Orion M 42.

Herschel extended the work of Messier and the earlier pioneers in this field of astronomy. By 1802, some 2,500 nebulae and clusters had been counted. The telescope revealed that where a handful of stars had previously been observed there were in fact hundreds. And what about the misty patches that defeated the viewer's instruments? Did they too consist of stars? After much contemplation Herschel decided that these misty areas were not star-filled. Indeed, he spoke of blank regions in the heavens. Thus there were star regions and nonstar regions. But this was one of the lesser problems that astronomers like Herschel faced. The greater was to decide upon the interrelationships among all the new-found celestial objects. Where did our solar system belong in this universe that seemed to grow bewilderingly vaster each time some observer of genius, such as Herschel, peeped through his telescope at the sky.

Huygens expressed the then dangerous thought that the universe might well consist of thousands of suns around which planets revolved, making up a collection of universes scattered throughout space. An Englishman, Thomas Wright, who had in his day been many things — clock maker, sailor, copper engraver — hazarded a guess that all the heavenly bodies that occupied space fitted into a bun-like shape. He was trying to account for the sight we have all seen in the skies, rarely without wonder — the Milky Way. He thought that as we started out at the broadest part of the bun, we took in the greatest number of stars, and it was this closely packed region of space that constituted the Milky Way.

In 1755, the German philosopher Immanuel Kant (1724–1804) echoed in more elaborate form what both Huygens and Wright before him had suggested. Kant said that space was not occupied by just one bun-shaped assortment of heavenly bodies but by countless such assortments at unimaginable distances from each other. His concept now seems to us very up-to-date, especially as he believed each of his star assortments could be identified with the white wisps of nebulae that we see. Kant's was really an inspired piece of guesswork for there is no evidence that he had emulated Herschel and searched space with a telescope.

Herschel put down his ideas on the subject only after he had carried out laborious and systematic observations. He called his book dealing with them *On the Construction of the Heavens* (1785), and he endorsed Wright's bun-shape theory, adding that the bun's edges were irregular and showed two sizable indentations that he assumed were the two branches of the Milky Way visible to any observer.

To make this deduction, Herschel set a "grid pattern" over the northern skies, breaking them up into 3,400 small areas. With amazing patience he counted the stars in each. Some regions, he felt convinced, had a star density about a hundred times greater than others. He inferred, therefore, that the stars in the "under-dense" regions were one hundred times as far away as were the stars in the "over-dense" regions, taking all stars to be about equidistant from each other, and to possess the same degree of absolute luminosity. If we look at a star X and decide it is half as bright as star Y we are considering only their apparent brightness, which results from star X being twice as far from us as star Y.

The tremendous imaginative vision of Herschel, who longed to penetrate the outermost frontiers of space and study its entirety, irritated his learned contemporaries and failed to strike in them the smallest spark. His speculations about the shape of the universe, even of the universes, in space seemed to them far-fetched. He died at eighty-four, disappointed with his efforts, which he himself had become inclined to distrust after consideration of all the criticism leveled at him. Almost a hundred years had to pass before an astronomer of our own age took up once again the themes that had filled so completely the head of William Herschel in the last quarter of his life.

The great days of the astronomers who wielded their telescopes were dimmed with the passing of Herschel. There seemed no new worlds to conquer, no new horizons left to scan. Then, unexpectedly, suddenly the elements of new drama gathered. There was, after all, to be a final fling for the astronomy of the telescope. In 1820, a French mathematician called Alexis Bouvard (1767–1843) set to work on the tables of Uranus, which goes around the sun in eighty-four years, and which had by then been observed over about half this course. It soon became obvious that something odd was going on. The tables of Bouvard appeared to be telling a story different from the one being acted out in the skies. The forecasts for the other planets were proving correct to within a few seconds but those for Uranus were out by 2 minutes of the arc in 1845. What was luring Uranus off its track? Since it could not be the perturbations of Jupiter or Saturn it had to be those of some other planet that had so far gone unspotted. The directors of the great laboratories at Greenwich and at Paris concurred.

The sole method of placing the unknown Planet X was to investigate the size and direction of the force that was disturbing Uranus. By employing mathematics of formidable difficulty, it might be possible to glean the mass of X, and the site it was occupying in space. The mind was staggered by the complications likely to arise in the manipulation of figures and equations. The man who slew successfully the mathematical monster was a Frenchman, Urbain-Jean-Joseph Le Verrier (1811–77), like the great Laplace himself, a Norman. He started life as an engineer in the State Tobacco Department but ended up, almost accidentally, as a lecturer in astronomy at the *École Polytechnique* which turned out to be an ideal berth. He adored figures and for him relaxation meant juggling with rows of numbers and producing answers — often out of his head — to the diabolical calculations he set himself. In order to recover from the fatigue of these efforts he played the violin, for he was an accomplished musician.

Invited by François Arago, Director of the Paris Observatory, to undertake the mathematics involved in the location of Planet X, he started off in 1844. He could attribute only 20 minutes of the 120 minutes of arc by which Uranus strayed to the action of Jupiter and Saturn. He deduced that its remaining deviation of 100 minutes of arc was due to the action of Planet X. On August 31, 1846, after wrestling with his figures, he declared that Planet X ought to be visible at a point in the heavens which he specified exactly. He declared also that Planet X took some 217 years to go around the sun. Moreover, he gave its mass in relation to the mass of the sun.

People who had eagerly been following his wizardry were dumbfounded. They could hardly credit that a man sitting in his study and burning the midnight oil could possibly come up with such assured answers. The rest was comparatively simple. A German astronomer, Johann Gottfried Galle (1812–1910), did just what Le Verrier advised: he trained his telescope on the spot the French scientist had indicated. A new planet "swam into his ken" when on September 23, 1846, he surveyed the skies. It was given the name *Neptune*. Le Verrier could hardly have supplied more effective testimony of the marvelous powers of science. Saturn, 887,100,000 miles from the sun had been the farthest known point of our system until Herschel placed Urnus at 1,785,000,000 miles from the sun. Now it was calculated that the newly discovered Neptune was 2,797,000 miles from the sun. Our universe had been extended in breathtaking succession since the days of Galileo and Kepler, just over two centuries before.

Sadly, Le Verrier's astounding feat was darkened by a bitter controversy with his English colleagues. When the presence of Planet X was first suspected, George Bidell Airy (1801–92), Director of the Greenwich Observatory, requested John Couch Adams (1819–92) to perform the calculations necessary to bring it to light. Adams completed his task in 1845, but his results were never published because his manuscript had been put aside in one of Airy's drawers. Yet it was later ascertained that he had emulated Le Verrier and reached the due answer. For this tragic piece of neglect, nobody could be blamed except the Englishmen themselves; Le Verrier was quite entitled to the fame and the honors that fell to him in so generous a share.

Part Four: 2

NEWTON, who argued against Huygens's Wave Theory of Light because he said waves could lap around corners whereas light could not, doubted the likelihood of an achromatic lens ever being made. But an amateur, an Essex magistrate called Chester Moor Hall (1703–71), showed practically how this very thing could be done. Newton had demonstrated that white light consisted of various colors and until about the middle of the eighteenth century, when Hall found the way to combat this effect, the image falling upon the object glass of a telescope broke into several colored images. To neutralize this tendency, astronomers used longer instruments, but clearly there is a limit to length. Thus ensued a period of stagnation in the history of the telescope.

Hall and a professional optician, John Dollond (1706–

61), appear to have been contemplating simultaneously but separately the problems raised by dispersion of light through refraction. Hall thought in terms of another lens to gather into a single image all the images that were formed with the biconvex objective lens. He tried out a biconcave lens of heavy glass with a lead base at the front of the objective. Its highly refractive powers "canceled out" the numerous colored images produced by the biconvex objective glass and thus ensured better focus. Like many inventors before and since, Hall was confronted by a challenger who claimed priority.

Whenever this happens, the dispute generally becomes acrimonious and the issue is rarely ever definitely settled, as, for example, in the case of the discovery of Neptune. Was it Le Verrier or was it John Couch Adams? Hall's rival for the honor was, of course, Dollond, who, it appears, had heard of Hall's experiments through George Bass, who actually ground the lenses that Hall combined to achieve achromatism. Hall explained that he got his idea through study of the human eye and, by 1729, had already found the two kinds of glasses he needed to produce something like the result he was after. By 1733, he had gone a step further using flint glass for the concave part and crown glass for the convex. Thus, a convex lens of crown glass cemented to a concave lens of flint glass with its higher refractive index largely disposed of chromatic aberration.

We need not here go into the ins and outs of the quarrels that occurred when it came to patenting an invention that many were convinced was Hall's. In 1758, Dollond read to the Royal Society a paper on the theme of achromatism and the patent was awarded to him. The mathematics behind the discovery were not worked out until 1760, when a Swedish scholar, Samuel Klingenstierna of Uppsala, constructed the theory. It is said, however, that both Clairaut and d'Alembert had already provided much of the theoretical groundwork involved.

Dollond, a silk manufacturer, who had come to England from France, was now ready to profit by Hall's invention. Yet he was being delayed because, though crown glass, which was white with a silica base, was not hard to obtain, flint glass for the concave lens was practically unobtainable.

The ingenuity of a Swiss, Pierre Louis Guinand (1748–1824), helped to make good the deficiency. Guinand started life making wooden cases for clocks; then he turned to casting clock bells because it was paying work and came across the method of stirring to keep homogeneous the metal of which the bells were made, meaning that all parts should consist of metal of the same sort where a mixture was used. Guinand wondered whether it might not be possible to apply this method to glass. Already at twenty he had become interested in the optician's trade and had tried his hand at it in small ways. But not until 1798, when he was fifty, did he first use a mushroom-shaped stirrer in making optical glass. It was not very successful and he went on trying out various kinds of stirrers until at last, in 1805, he devised just what was wanted, a hollow cylinder of burnt fireclay in which molten glass could be stirred by a hook-ended iron rod.

Since homogeneity (the even distribution throughout of all the components) was the key to the production of high-quality glass without the "veining" that often marred it; and since the system of stirring evolved by Guinand ensured even distribution throughout of the silica, lead oxide, and potash that were the chief ingredients of flint glass, its manufacture in quantity became possible. Heavier materials could be added to mixtures because of stirring, which also prevented troublesome air bubbles from forming. The great advantage of bubble-free glass was that more light could pass through it.

Guinand did not have the resources to develop his invention, so he went to Bavaria, Germany, in order to produce lenses for a German firm. Collaborating with the manager of the firm, Joseph von Fraunhofer (1787–1826), he far advanced his stirring method. The details of Guinand's discovery remained a secret that glass producers in many countries were anxious to procure. After Guinand's death in 1824, a French firm bought it from his son and not until 1837, did the secret reach England through a Birmingham firm, Chance Brothers, which, in turn, bought it from the French. But the full benefits of the purchase were not felt until George Bontemps, the original purchaser and the most celebrated glass technologist of his day, left France after the Revolution of 1848 to join Chance who built a special plant for him to manage. Soon the firm enjoyed a wide reputation for its "hard crown" and "dense flint" for telescopes.

Meanwhile, Fraunhofer created the astronomical refractor of the type we use to this day. In December, 1817, he completed manufacture of an object glass with a diameter of 9½ inches and a focus of 14 feet, 6 inches. His new achromatic lens was, at the time, unique because never before had there been an instrument with such a large aperture and such short focal length. The Russians bought the Fraunhofer object glass and used it to equip the observatory at Dorpat (modern Tartu, Esthonia). Its highest benefit to the astronomer was accuracy of an order never before achieved. It was mounted as an equatorial, meaning it could follow the diurnal course of a star, without the operator having to move a finger since it was regulated by a clockwork mechanism. Operators and apparatus were housed in a movable dome with a breach that could be opened as necessary. With the growing availability of efficient telescopes, a whole crop of observatories sprang up in Europe and in America and observers strove to discover new stars and clear up remaining obscurities in the knowledge of our solar system.

In Germany the firm of Merz and Mahler produced (1839) an objective with a diameter of 38 centimeters for the Russians, to equip the observatory at Pulkovo. Thus they improved upon an earlier objective some 32 centimeters in diameter, which the Frenchman Cauchois had produced for the Cambridge Observatory in 1835. The pioneer efforts of Fraunhofer were soon outstripped, particularly in America, where the great optician Alvan C. Clarke (1804–87) bettered the accomplishments of his celebrated European rivals. Clarke, in Massachusetts, was quietly busying himself with his career as a painter of miniatures when an amateur astronomer, an Englishman named Dawes, ran into him and discovered that his talent for grinding lenses far excelled his talent for painting miniatures. He proclaimed to the world that as a lens grinder, Clarke was supreme. Soon Clarke was commissioned to make lenses for a number of observatories both in his own country and elsewhere. He linked up with the French firm that had inherited the traditions and the methods of Guinand and the glass he used was supplied by them at high cost.

The European Industrial Revolution was showing every sign of gathering pace in the opening years of the nineteenth century and by the middle years of the century it got under way in America, also. Earlier the "cottage industries" fell under control of businessmen who gathered them together into money-making units. The old picture of cottagers independently plying their trades and selling in the neighboring markets was a thing of the past. The resulting expansion of money, and the obvious benefits of heavy industries, which were soon commanding the whole field, ushered in the era of nineteenth-century capitalism and "free enterprise," which once again resulted in the expansion of money on an undreamed-of scale. On the other hand, the vast majority of people were forced into the position of wage-earners, at the mercy of whatever gambles their employers chose to take on the road to personal fortunes, and of the ups and downs of a system whose instability remains to this day seemingly incurable. In America, the situation differed from that in Europe. Development of a new country presented almost unlimited opportunities, everything was "wide open," and the tycoon sprouted in every field of enterprise.

The tycoons both of America and of Europe harnessed science to their money chariots. They exploited it as a source of wealth rather than as a source of benefit for the common good. Yet science profited, if by the way, from their undertakings. In America particularly, which had only just emerged through the doorway of adventure by "opening up the West," business magnates were less cautious than their more conservative European counterparts. They were prepared to invest heavily in science because they predicted big returns out of it for growing industries. Alvan Clark ground the object glass for a telescope built out of a fortune left by James Lick, the piano king, who boasted that he had put music into every other American front parlor. Charles T. Yerkes, the railway king, financed the observatory outside Chicago named after him, while yet another tycoon, Hooker, paid a great deal towards the magnificent 100-inch telescope at Mount Wilson in California. To moneyed men, such benefactions were promising investments, status-symbols, and a means of perpetuating name and fame. Their donations were, on the other hand, gratefully received by scientists who needed the equipment to pursue their inquiries.

Part Four: 3

THE prestige of Newton, for a long time, kept Huygens's Wave Theory of Light in the background. Men like the English scholar Francis Wollaston (1766–1828) tried to revive Huygens's idea, only to meet with strenuous opposition. Broadly speaking, two different schools of thought existed at the beginning of the nineteenth century. To one, light was a wave motion; it behaved like a continuous succession of waves. To the other, it was like a flight of fast-moving particles, or a hail of bullets. Thus, Wave Theory was confronted by Corpuscular Theory or Theory of Minute Bodies or Particles.

Thomas Young (1773–1829), a native of Somerset, England, carried Huygens's theory forward by saying that light waves were more than pulses — they were continuous, periodic waves. But what if there were more than one sort of wave motion? He thought that if two sorts of waves from different sources coincided the net result would amount to a combination of both their motions. Young trained as a doctor and practiced in London, but did not find medicine to his taste, so he took up an appointment as professor at the Royal Institution. His medical training and his interest in physics drew him toward some of the problems of sight. He described astigmatism caused by an eye defect that keeps light rays from being brought into proper focus, and he also put forward the theory that color perception depends on three kinds of nerve fibers in the retina that respond to red, green, and violet light. In 1801, he discovered the principle of interference of light.

But it was a Frenchman, Augustin Jean Fresnel (1788–1827), who really laid the foundations of our modern theory. Fresnel was born at Broglie in Normandy and educated at Caen. He became an engineer only to lose his job because he expressed his opposition to Napoleon's seizure of power upon his return to France from the Island of Elba in March, 1815. In that same year Fresnel began his optical researches and, by using mathematics with consummate skill, managed to dispose of many objections to the Wave Theory of Light. He received scanty recognition for his work during his lifetime and many of his papers were not printed by the Academy of Sciences until long after his death. He accepted his neglect philosophically and wrote to Young that all the compliments of famous people could hardly equal the pleasure he derived from arriving at the truth by means of theory or of confirming theory by means of experiment.

With Fresnel's principles of light well settled the Scottish physicist James Clerk Maxwell (1831–79), in 1860, identified light with electric waves and supported his theory with the necessary mathematical proofs. Clerk Maxwell, born in Edinburgh and educated at the University there and at Cambridge, graduated with high distinction. He first took a teaching post in Aberdeen, later joining the staff of King's College, London. Having retired to his family estate in Scotland, he was persuaded to come out of retirement and take a chair at Cambridge, where he associated himself closely with the foundation of the world-renowned Cavendish Laboratory. Some have criticized him as a "pencil and paper" scientist; they have compared him unfavorably with Michael Faraday (1791–1867), who made his discoveries in electricity as a result of his passion for experiment. Clerk Maxwell was both theoretician and experimenter, a man gifted with vast imagination and a deep love of science. Modern color photography can, for example, be traced back to an experiment Maxwell performed in 1861, and his theory of light as electromagnetic waves led directly to the discovery, by Heinrich Hertz (1857–94), of radio waves. We who enjoy the benefits of radio and television appreciate just what this discovery means in our own lives.

Today, having developed the method of *L*ight *A*mplification by *S*timulated *E*mission *R*adiation (laser) to produce a highly directional, monochromatic (literally one-colored) and coherent light beam, scientists appreciate even more what Clerk Maxwell taught. He maintained that the behavior of a light beam could be predicted solely by its wave length and its velocity in the material through which it traveled. We know that in transparent materials, an intense light beam, like sound and radio waves, generates overtones, or harmonics as we call them, of the original light frequency. We know, too, that in the presence of matter, two light beams can react with each other, and that the electromagnetic wave of which light is made up consists of an electrical part and a magnetic counterpart, both locked in step at right angles to each other and oscillating together. We know, furthermore, that we can alter the velocity of light by applying an additional electrical or magnetic field, and that light radiates in discrete (separate or discontinuous) bundles called photons. Photons interact with each other, colliding and scattering.

Such knowledge stems largely from Clerk Maxwell's exciting work which surprised people of his day by bringing optics and electricity closer together than had ever been thought possible. This and other significant events foreshadowed important developments in microscopy. Until the end of the eighteenth century, nobody had demonstrated that light was both visible and invisible, that outside the band of radiations we can detect with our eyes are invisible radiations, such as ultraviolet, infrared, X-rays, and gamma rays, that behave like light — except in one important respect. All such radiations travel at the same speed (about 186,000 miles per second), but they have different wave lengths. William Herschel, in 1801, found the infrared of sunlight, its invisible heat rays. At about the same time, Johann Wilhelm Ritter (1776–1810), the German physicist, spurred on by Herschel's discovery, found ultraviolet rays beyond the violet end of the spectrum. Both scientists had obtained their results by observing the heating effect of these radiations. Ritter, for example, detected ultraviolet through its effect upon chloride of silver.

Meanwhile, since the correction of chromatic aberration, telescope objectives had been growing bigger and microscope objectives smaller. The very smallness of the microscope objectives tended to emphasize their imperfections; this drawback had to be overcome. The nature of light waves limits the powers of the microscope and diffraction frustrates the realization of the "perfect" image. Moreover, an image remains indistinct no matter how greatly it is magnified. Furthermore, effective magnification is governed by powers of resolution. Opticians strove to add brilliancy to the small microscope objective, appreciating that the greater the numerical aperture, the greater the resolution. (Numerical aperture means both the angle of the light, and the refractive index of the medium from which the light passes into the objective.) The great American optician Charles A. Spencer (1813–81), laboring in a small back room with very little money, succeeded in improving microscope objectives by devising higher apertures. He also obtained better color correction by using fluorite combinations in his lenses. His pupil, Robert B. Tolles (1822–83), and his son, Herbert R. Spencer (1849–1900), carried on his work, producing objectives of the highest type, both for telescope and microscope. Herbert Spencer founded his own firm, which has an important place in the history of American optics.

In much research with the microscope, the whole field of view is illuminated and the objects under examination show up as colored pictures or as shadows against a white background. This is *bright-field microscopy*. In certain circumstances, the researcher uses a dark field and the objects under examination appear to be self-lit. This is *dark-field microscopy*. Some objects are indeed self-illuminating, such as plants and animals touched by phosphorescence. Those which are not deflect light from some source outside reaching into the microscope. But to procure dark-field illumination the light had to enter so obliquely that it could not directly reach the microscope objective. On the other hand, it had to be bright enough to render clear the object to be investigated. It was Joseph Jackson Lister, father of a famous son, Joseph Lister (we shall refer more fully to him in due course), who in 1830, began dark-field microscopy; but Francis Wenham (1823–1908), about 1853, made this form of microscopy possible for far higher powers.

In Italy, Giovanni Battista Amici (1786–1863, and in Britain, a Scotsman, Sir David Brewster (1781–1868), made many efforts to improve microscope objectives, which are of two kinds: dry and wet. With the dry objective there is air between objective and cover glass or object. Amici and Brewster used liquids for the immersion of objectives. The liquids are sometimes water, sometimes thickened cedarwood oil. Cedarwood oil is suitable because it has the same refractive index as that of glass so that light suffers no refraction when it passes from the glass slide and the cover glass into the immersing liquid. The advantage of immersion was that it made possible increase in aperture. Why should increase in aperture result in improvement? The answer is contained in the single word *resolution*. The resolution, or resolving power, of an objective is its capacity to show up as distinctly as possible details of structure. The more "separate" these details, the better the eye can appreciate them. We must mention here that Robert Tolles played a big part in securing this increase in aperture which so much helped scientists who were users of the microscope.

In reviewing the developments of the microscope during the nineteenth century, however, we cannot avoid the feeling that the triumphs belong largely to Ernst Abbe (1840–1905), the German physicist who was born at Eisenach in Thuringia, and was educated at Göttingen and at Jena. Professor of astronomy at Jena, he there began an association with the optician Carl Zeiss, in 1866. Ten years later, he became Zeiss's partner, and after Zeiss's death, he became sole proprietor of the firm. Financed liberally by the German government, and assisted by Schott, a practical glassmaker of great skill, Abbe and Zeiss were able to outdo even Spencer in making new types of glass.

Abbe was responsible for apochromatic objectives consisting of special forms of glass and a natural mineral, such as fluorite, which make almost perfect color and spherical corrections. With ordinary achromatic objectives, rays of two colors of the spectrum are united into one focus. With apochromatic objectives, rays of three colors of the spectrum are thus combined.

In 1902, F. E. Ives proposed the basis of the system for modern binocular eye pieces, and in 1935, Fritz Zernike, a physicist who won the Nobel Prize in 1953, successfully applied phase contrast. Means have to be found of lessening or of increasing contrast with specimens under examination. For example, if the contrast is too great, the idea is to reduce it by using some sort of screen of the same color as

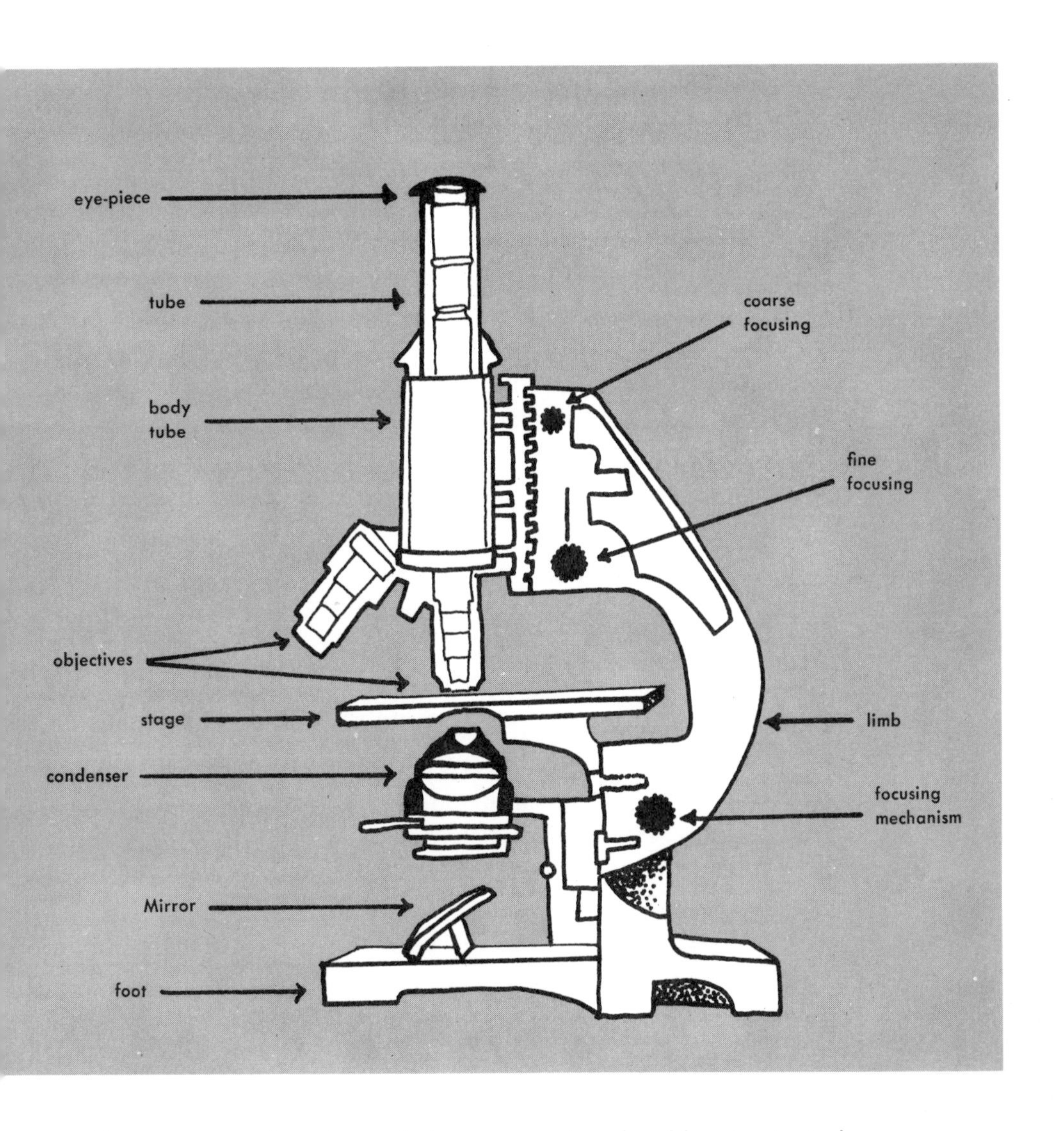

The microscope, like other optical instruments from hand lens to giant telescope, depends upon the ability of its parts to refract light.

that of the object. Screens can "choose" certain wave lengths of light which they will, like traffic policemen, pass on, while stopping or absorbing others that are unwanted.

The work of Herschel, Ritter, Clerk Maxwell, and others, kept bringing its reward well into the twentieth century, and it was to provide alternatives to the standard light microscope, which remains, nevertheless, the stock apparatus of every laboratory. Was it possible to use invisible rays in microscopy? Would ultramicroscopic radiations, which have a smaller wave length than visible light be able to reveal objects too small for investigation under the ordinary microscope? Only in 1925, did Joseph Edwin Barnard (1869–1949) show that ultraviolet-ray microscopy was practicable. He adapted a reflecting microscope to ultramicroscopy and succeeded in photographing with it some of the larger viruses.

Viruses are microbes that can flourish only within the living cell and cause such diseases as poliomyelitis or measles. Scientists are still arguing about whether they are plant, animal, or some "in-between" form of life. Viruses long eluded search because they are so minute, and when we describe them as "larger" or "smaller" we speak of them comparatively to their own small size. The benefit of ultramicroscopy is that it enables us to catch sight of these little creatures because its shorter wave length offers better power of resolution than do the wave lengths of light microscopes. We can thus bring more detail into our vision.

About 1830, an Irish mathematician, W. R. Hamilton (1805–65), a neat, meticulous man who had been educated at Trinity College, Dublin (and who had actually detected a mistake in the work of Laplace), suggested that many parallels exist between optics and mechanics. Almost a century later (1924), the French scientist and Nobel Prize winner, Louis de Broglie (b. 1892), like Laplace a Norman, contemplated the two rival theories of light: the continuous succession of waves and the flight of particles. The work of Max Planck (1858–1947) and Albert Einstein (1879–1955) led scientists to accept that light behaved in a manner that might fit both these theories, but de Broglie was prepared to go further. He said that material particles, like electrons, possessed some sort of wave character. Matter resembled light and could behave either as waves or as "corpuscles," meaning like a flight of particles. Some two years later, the Austrian scientist Erwin Schrödinger (1887–1961) combined the ideas of both Hamilton and de Broglie. He advanced the theory of wave mechanics, especially in its application to atomic structure.

Schrödinger had at his command the theory for constructing an electron microscope, but the practicability of such an instrument was demonstrated by Hans Busch who, after spending fifteen years studying the trajectory of electrons in magnetic fields, published his results. He stated that magnetic or electrical fields having axial symmetry can act as "lenses" for electrons. Such "lenses" had to be immaterial because electrons move freely only in a vacuum. In 1927, he went on to make such a magnetic "lens" and later, two American researchers verified Busch's claims. Such were the beginnings of yet another method for "seeing small."

Electron microscopes can be constructed because, like light waves, electronic waves are transmitted in straight lines. They can also be focused by electromagnets, rather as light can be focused by means of lenses. Moreover, the focus can be varied by increasing or lessening the strength of the current in the electromagnet. Since electronic waves cannot be picked up by the eye they have to be made visible by means of a fluorescent screen or photographic plates. In this sense the electron microscope resembles the projection microscope. The image offered to view has already been formed. In the mid nineteen-thirties, Ernst Ruzcka described, and later built, the first electron microscope with an electromagnetic lens (as opposed to an electrostatic lens, which can also be employed in these instruments). A Belgian, L. Marton, is said first to have examined biological specimens with this new type of apparatus, and F. Krause afterward obtained electron micrographs of various materials. For some time, no electron microscope provided better powers of resolution than did the light microscope. Only in 1955, did E. Driest and H. O. Müller, using a Ruzcka apparatus, surpass the light microscope in this respect.

In truth, both the electron microscope and the light microscope have their place in science. For one thing, living matter cannot be studied under the electron microscope because specimens for inspection have to undergo a form of preparation that kills them. On the other hand, the comparative largeness of light waves places limitations on what the light microscope can do. Although a light wave is small enough (about one fifty-thousandth of an inch or less), it remains some 2,000 times as large as an atom. Thus, electron waves can be considerably shorter, some as little as one-tenth of an atomic diameter. The magnifying power of the electron microscope is very great, although it is rarely used "at full stretch" because better results can be obtained by exercising its magnifying powers to a lesser degree. Put in another way, it magnifies up to 200,000 diameters; but it is more effective, for example, in the investigation of viruses, if operated at about a quarter of that strength.

Clerk Maxwell's theories concerning electromagnetic waves, and Heinrich Hertz's success in producing them (1886), may be regarded as the acorn out of which grew the mighty oak we label nowadays as electronics, with its innumerable military and industrial applications. Both industry and science fed the growth of electronics. Already in 1884, Thomas Alva Edison (1847–1931), the great American inventor, born in Ohio of Dutch and Scottish parentage, at work in his laboratory at Menlo Park, observed that the glowing filament of an electric bulb would keep a positive but not a negative charge. By sealing a metallic plate into the bulb he was able to pass a current from the plate to the filament, although not the other way round.

Why this happened could be accounted for by the electron theory of the English physicist Sir J. J. Thomson, who was Cavendish Professor at Cambridge University and Master of Trinity, the college where Newton himself had received his higher education. The heated filament wire gave off electrons that moved across to the plate only if the filament was charged positively. On the other hand, the unheated plate was not able to discharge electrons even when it was charged negatively. In 1905, de Forest improved upon

Edison's first electric valve and made the triode, a valve with three electrodes, which made it possible for electromagnetic waves to be both generated and amplified.

We would not be claiming too much if we say that the introduction of the triode valve, deriving from Edison's original observation, started a revolution in our lives, for it made practicable broadcasting, radiotelephony, and every kind of work calling for the use of high frequency. The significant benefit of the shorter wave length is that it can be directed or beamed, and increasing ability to control and direct electromagnetic waves gave us, ultimately, the power to "see" the unseen. It added a new dimension to vision. We can, as a result, "see" objects (spacecraft, for example) at untold distances, with the help of the cathode-ray oscillograph, which also sprang out of Sir J. J. Thomson's experiments. The cathode-ray tube, as we more familiarly know it, "makes electrical events visible." It has been described as a "time microscope," which enables us to follow, well out of our range of sight, by electrical means, happenings that undergo constant changes whose nature would otherwise be hidden from us.

In 1895, an Italian, Guglielmo Marconi (1874–1937), experimenting near Bologna, managed to send a wireless message over a distance of about one mile. The following year, he went to Britain and there continued his experiments. It has been said that Marconi's was the triumph of the gifted amateur possessed of unreasonable optimism. Had he been a professional scientist, and had he been put off by the insuperable obstacles forseen by professional scientists, he might never have ventured at all. But he demonstrated his faith by forming, in 1898, the Marconi Wireless Telegraph Company. In 1899, he actually sent a wireless message across the English Channel, justifying thereby his profound optimism, and his belief that the prospects of success were good. In 1901, he sent signals all the way from Poldhu in Cornwall to St. John's, Newfoundland. By 1918, he had made contact with Australia, "down under," in the other half of the world.

Wireless telegraphy had become a reality. Messages were soon reaching every quarter of the globe in the code devised by the American S. F. B. Morse (1791–1872), who, in 1836, also invented the electromagnetic telegraph for sending messages along wires by means of electrical impulses.

Meteorologists, keen to discover more about the behavior of thunderstorms and other disturbances in the atmosphere, started to employ directed waves for their investigations, while communications engineers explored the possibility of beaming signals to distant parts. However, an intriguing question remained unanswered until the 1920's. Did radio waves sweep directly on from one place to another, so to speak, "in a straight line?" Or were they in some way reflected? And if they were reflected as scientists were inclined to think, what was their reflector?

During the 1920's, Sir Edward Appleton (b. 1892), son of a Yorkshire millhand who won his way to Cambridge on scholarships and there worked with Rutherford himself, was able to show that radio waves were, in fact, reflected, and that their reflector was the ionosphere, the earth's "envelope," which consists of layers made up of ions or moving particles carrying charges of positive or negative electricity.

Indeed, in 1923, Appleton and M. A. F. Barnett "radio-located" the Heaviside layer whose existence had, in 1902, been predicted by the physicist Sir Oliver Heaviside. Later, two Americans, G. Bright and M. A. Tuve, in Washington, actually measured the height of the Heaviside layer. By 1932, the radio-pulse technique had become standard in investigations of this kind.

Developments in radio enabled ground stations to take bearings on transmissions and to "place" their origins. Direction Finding (D/F) became an invaluable asset to air navigation, among other things. Thus, three suitably located D/F stations could "fix" the position of an aircraft by obtaining, on the despatch of a long enough signal from it, bearings that intersected to form a triangle. Operators at a central control to which these bearings were passed could then "fix" the position of the machine within that triangle, using an appropriately mapped table.

During the Battle of Britain in the summer of 1940, R.A.F. ground controllers were able to plot overland the course of their interceptor fighters by means of the triangulation method. One aircraft in a formation switched on a device known as "Pip Squeak," which for ten seconds in every two or three minutes automatically sent out a shrill note on which three ground stations took bearings. The bearings were "spoken" over landline to a triangulation room and the position of the formation "fixed." A succession of "fixes" indicated by arrows on a plotting table, yielded a track. Accordingly, ground controllers could give pilots the directions they needed to intercept the German invaders.

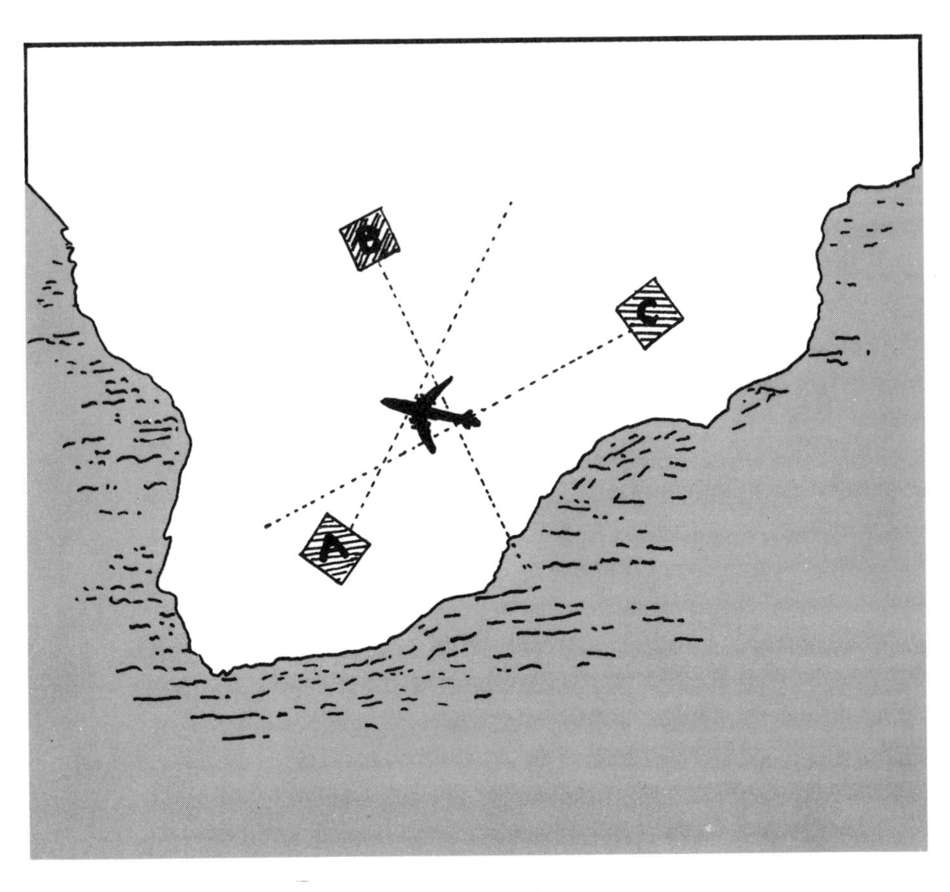

"Seeing" by means of radio waves

Direction-finding stations A, B and C take bearings on the aircraft. They intersect to form a triangle. Their information, set out on a plotting table, at a central control room, enables operators to "fix" the aircraft's position.

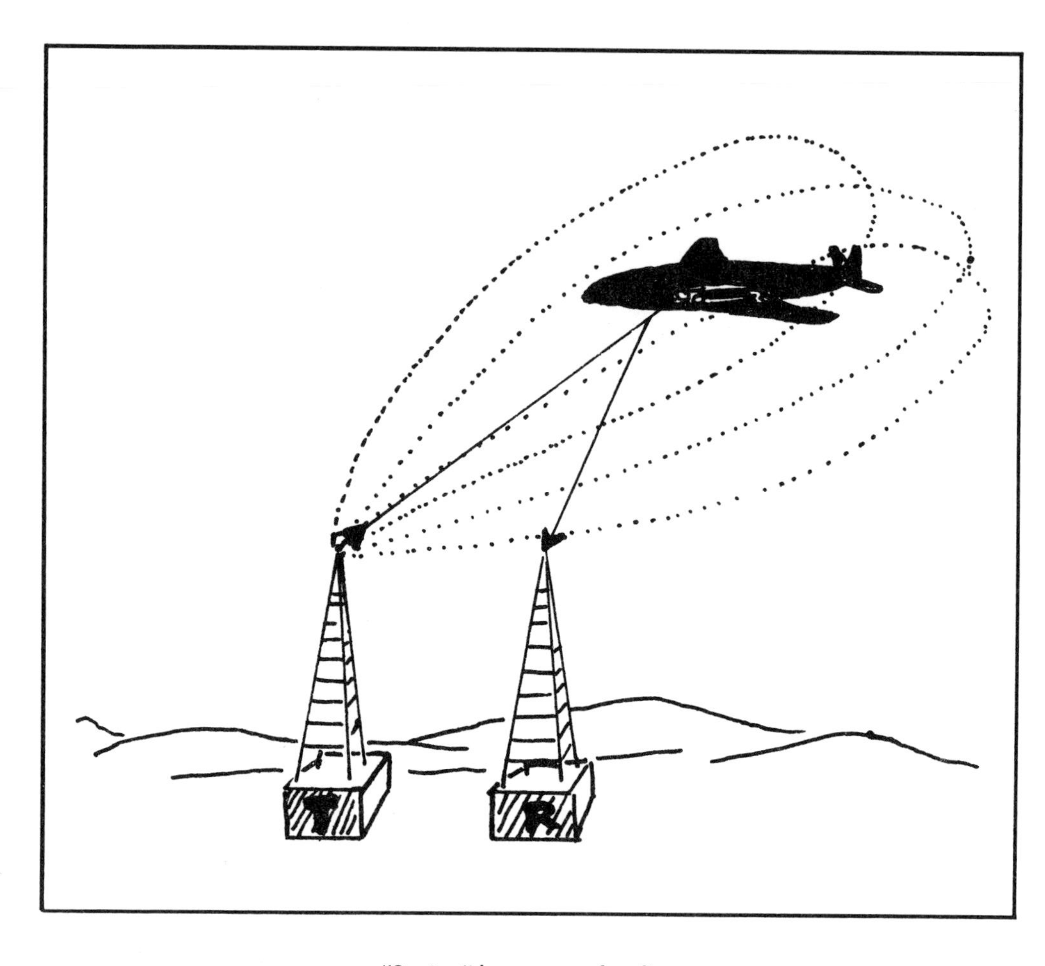

"Seeing" by means of radio waves

Radio waves from a transmitter, T, "echo" back from the aircraft to the receiver, R. The time taken for this to happen, measured in fractions of a second and shown on a cathode-ray tube in the form of a time base, enables distance away of the aircraft to be computed.

This, in simplest terms, is how radar works.

It was one way of "seeing" the unseen. But there was to be even better. Scientists working with the pulse technique had observed that all solid and liquid bodies reflect radio waves when "flooded" by them. Radio waves are, of course, not influenced by darkness, cloud, or fog. The reflection could be seen on a cathode-ray tube as an "echo." Now, the speed of the pulses is the same as that of light: 186,000 miles per second. If the time taken for pulses to echo back from an object could be measured, then its distance could be ascertained. So could its bearing and an approximation of its height.

The vulnerability of the British Isles to attack by a powerful German *Luftwaffe* stimulated research into such matters. Was there a possibility of detecting by radio-location enemy aircraft before they made landfall so that the defenses could be mustered in advance? In February, 1935, Sir Robert Watson-Watt (b. 1892), a Scottish scientist, suggested that radio-location might well be able to detect aircraft while they were still about fifty miles away, and perhaps ships also. By 1939, using the comparatively long 10-meter wave length, the British had the most exposed part of their eastern and southeastern coastline protected by a chain of stations capable of detecting aircraft up to a distance of 35 miles at a height of 10,000 feet. From the air, ships could be detected at a range of about nine miles, which soon increased to some thirty miles. Apparatus for anti-aircraft guns to shoot "blind," and for searchlights to pick out targets "blind" were gradually devised.

Such were the beginnings of Radiolocution or Radar

(*R*adio *A*ngle *D*irection *a*nd *R*ange), as the Americans came to call it.

One of the most interesting applications of radar enabled ground controllers to direct night fighters toward enemy bombers. Once within range, an operator in the fighter, using a radar apparatus provided in the machine, was able to "home" onto the attacker and thereby give his pilot the opportunity of sighting and firing at him.

Truly, man had acquired the power of "seeing" through the darkness — had extended his vision electrically to almost infinite distances. Short waves have given him an extra sense organ, enabling him thereby vastly to augment his perception of the universe itself, for radar in its most up-to-date forms supplies an indispensable aid to his exploration of space. With it he can check calculations of distance, for example, the precise distance from our earth to the moon and other celestial bodies. Radar has made navigation at sea and in the air safer. It is now possible to land an aircraft "blind" once the pilot has set its course down the runway. Radar also can be used for accurate mapping of terrain, and for various meteorological purposes.

Yet the startling innovations of science daily remind us that we are still only at the beginning. Satellites are now our "all-seeing eyes." They can be steered with unerring accuracy over any given point on earth. They can, moreover, be made to arrive there at any given time, often so that the sun is behind them in order to make it possible for the fine-focus cameras with which they are equipped to take photographs astonishing in both detail and clarity. One such satellite is reported to have recorded every phase of a launching from a cosmodrome. Once the photographs have been taken, they are ejected in a succession of capsules which can be picked up by an aircraft at a predetermined point. A striking feature of recent space flights has been the degree of vision of which the naked human eye appears to be capable. Astronauts have picked out specific locations and installations on earth with an ease that has confounded us. Our eyes possess powers of which we were previously unaware.

Infrared equipment of great ingenuity has also helped to extend our vision. Fitted in satellites, it is able to pick up traces of the hot exhaust gases emitted by rockets whenever they are launched. As we have seen, radiations are of three kinds: visible, invisible infrared, and actinic, or ultraviolet. All three possess the characteristics of visible light. They can be "thrown" across space, they refract, they reflect, and they can be impeded by a black surface. For example, the image of a black object will not darken silver salts, which explains why a photographic plate is a negative.

While ultraviolet is to be found in the X-rays that penetrate animal tissue and a number of other materials, infrared becomes heat rays when it produces heat as its most marked effect. When a black object impedes its radiation, the temperature usually goes up and the effect is particularly visible at the red end of the spectrum and the lesser affected areas of refraction.

The human eye, in conjunction with the brain, gives us the means of recognizing images, of analyzing them, and of following them. To see an object is to understand its nature far better. It is these functions of eye and brain that discoveries like radar, and the launching of space vehicles, have enlarged in recent days, in a fashion never before dreamed of. Even we who live in the midst of these prodigious scientific advances sometimes find it difficult to credit them as reality, not the imaginings of the writers of so-called science fiction.

Part Four: 4

THE microscope, it has been said, is supreme among modern optical instruments. Without it, modern medicine would be unthinkable. So would allied sciences like histology (study of tissues), pathology (study of diseased tissues and of diseases in general), protozoology (study of animals of the simplest types), bacteriology, virology (study of viruses), and molecular biology (study of the interior workings of the cell). Astronomy and the biological sciences have been the two main beneficiaries of improvements in lens grinding and in other aspects of optics. Yet sciences like chemistry, physics, mineralogy, and engineering find the microscope indispensable. As long ago as 1664, the English microscopist Henry Power first examined metal. "Look at a polished piece of gold, silver, steel, copper, tin, or lead," he advised, "and you see them all full of fissures and cavities and irregularities; but least of all in lead which is the closest and most compact solid body, probably in the world." Power went on to examine the sparks that fly when steel is struck and Hooke took up this topic again in his *Micrographia*.

The all-pervasiveness of the microscope today surprises nobody, for we accept it readily as "a pair of deep-seeing eyes," an extension of our own powers of vision. Once scientists realized that far more lay below the surface than they had ever dreamed of, it was a matter of time until they evolved the techniques of penetrating these below-surface secrets. Until the nineteenth century, the telescope had outshone the microscope. Then the microscope gained something like parity. How it did so is a story too long, too intricate, and too extensive for us to recount it in detail. We can consider only its main outlines.

Broadly speaking, the revolution in the biological sciences was brought about by the so-called Cell Theory of Scheiden and Schwann, by Darwin's Theory of Evolution and by Pasteur's Germ Theory. The microscope played a comparatively small part in the development of the Darwinian Theory that life started many millions of years ago with the simplest creatures or plants. These simple forms of life combined in ways unknown to us to produce the more complicated forms we know, including Man himself. The earth, it is nowadays reckoned, must be 4,500,000,000 to 5,000,000,000 years old. By contrast, Man is between 1,000,000 and 1,500,000 years old, a latecomer, indeed the latest comer, and probably descended from a small mammal. Species survived, Darwin said, by means of natural selection. Those that adapted best to their natural environment (and that they should adapt is all that nature asks of them) tended to thrive. Although new, subtle interrelationships between living things have come to light, the principles Darwin enunciated still apply in our consideration of life as a "grand design."

The Cell Theory of Schleiden and Schwann was, in a sense, anticipated by Hooke, Malpighi, and even Power. The English botanist Nehemiah Grew (1641–1712), actually drew plant cells, but it would be an exaggeration to name these scientists as pioneers of the Cell Theory. Oddly enough, a Frenchman, Marie François Xavier Bichat (1771–1802), who might be regarded as one of its truer pioneers, did not even use the microscope in his researches. He thought of animal tissue as a web. He used the French *tissu:* web, for it, but in order to keep the "classical" flavor of this sort of terminology, we finally coined a word not from the French, but from the Greek *histos:* web, from which we get *histology*.

Let us, for a moment, ask ourselves: What is a cell? A cell is a tiny portion of living matter, a unit of physical life, the unit of which all living things are composed. A jellylike substance known as protoplasm, consisting largely of proteins, is enclosed within a membrane — and already we have a cell. Within the cell is a little round body called a nucleus, without which most cells cannot reproduce themselves. They reproduce by dividing. The single cell divides into two, each of the two daughter cells again divides into two, making four, and so the process goes on indefinitely. Only the red blood cells of the body lack a nucleus, while the nucleus of the embryo contains a denser spot called the nucleolus. The shape of the cell is maintained by surface tension or by chemical action. Only recently have scientists begun fully to appreciate the marvelous complexity of cells which we have described in a very simple way.

Felice Fontana, in 1781, spotted the nucleus of a cell. It is said he may even have seen a nucleolus. Rudolf Wagner certainly described the nucleolus in 1835. Ferdinand Lucas Bauer first drew for us a picture showing the nucleus of an orchid cell. The Scottish botanist Robert Brown (1773–1848), coined the term *nucleus*. "Clear jelly," or protoplasm, was noted by Felix Dujardin as far back as 1835. Johannes Muller (1801–58), and his pupil, Friedrich Gustave Jakob Henle (1809–85), both indicated that different kinds of cells existed, for example, in the human skin. But as yet the Cell Theory as such had not been advanced. This was the work of Schleiden, and of Schwann who was a friend of Henle and a pupil of Johannes Muller. Schleiden and Schwann used to meet for dinner and after-dinner chats during the course of which they discussed their ideas. Schwann was responsible for carrying the Cell Theory as far as it went and for suggesting that animals consist of various types of cells, each type suited to a particular purpose.

The importance of the cell's protoplasm was gradually recognized. A Belgian botanist, Barthelmy Charles Dumortier, in 1832, observed cell division, which Hugo Mohl (1805–72) described in some detail three years later. Mohl also coined the word *protoplasm*. The Cell Theory had thus been building up piece by piece before Schleiden and Schwann, in 1839, gave it coherence, but it is on their declaration that modern cytology (study of cells) truly rests.

In 1814, John Hughes Bennett (1812–75), started to give courses on histology at Edinburgh University, using a microscope for his demonstrations. He first described leukemia, or "blood cancer" as it is sometimes called. Meanwhile, Karl von Rokitansky (1804–78), who spent his life in Vienna General Hospital, himself performed over 30,000 autopsies and collected records of more than 70,000 in all. Having analyzed this mass of material he wrote three volumes entitled *Manual of Pathological Anatomy* (1841–46), dealing in the first of these with his microscopical observations. But the true founder of modern cellular pathology is Rudolf Virchow (1821–1902), a German from Pomerania who, surprisingly enough, led the opposition to Chancellor Bismarck, in the Reichstag.

Rokitansky went badly astray because he knew nothing about cell division. He thought, as Schwann did, that new cells were born of some "primitive material." Virchow, on the other hand, was fortunate enough to appreciate the importance of cell division, which his scientific colleagues had not long before demonstrated. He gave as much time to microscopical studies as to performing autopsies. He attacked Rokitansky's ideas and approached pathology on a truly rational basis. He avoided thereby the trap, into which many scientists have fallen, of trying to present as reasonable, in terms of science, notions that have a place only in religion or in "tradition," and that are incapable of real definition or of scientific proof. Meanwhile, small but invaluable inventions had come to the aid of the microscopist — for example, the microtome, an instrument for cutting tissues into sections as thin as the microscopist desires. From the 1870's, methods of staining specimens in order the better to discern their true structure were also improved. The microscopists' tasks were thus eased.

Van Leeuwenhoek, the Danish scientist Otto Friedrich Müller (1730–84), and one or two others, appreciated that microbes of different sorts existed. What they did not realize was that microbes can cause disease; indeed, that a certain kind of microbe causes a certain kind of disease. In other words, they know nothing of specificity. About 1835–36 an Italian devotee of the microscope, Agostino Bassi (1773–1856), who was a lawyer turned civil servant, recognized that a certain infectious disease which killed silkworms was caused by a tiny living fungus. Some three years later, a German doctor, Johann Lucas Schönlein (1793–1864), announced that a certain skin disease was also induced by a fungus. The notion of tiny organisms outside the body giving rise to disease was in the air. But the true author of the Germ Theory of Disease was the Frenchman Louis Pasteur (1822–95), son of a tanner from the little French village of Dôle in the Jura Mountains. Though his school career was by no means distinguished, he worked enormously hard to pass his exams, and became a chemist. His early writings lead us to think that somehow he had a profound sense of his great destiny, and that he was always preparing himself to answer whenever fate knocked at the door.

He introduced himself to the scientific world by publishing papers about crystals, and he was a founder of stereochemistry, which deals with the composition of matter as it is affected by the relations of atoms in space. As a professor at the University of Lille in northern France, he began his studies on fermentation, which brought him fame but also exposed him to ferocious attack. The celebrated German chemist Justus von Liebig (1803–73) regarded fermentation as a form of chemical decomposition. But Pasteur, poring over his microscope in a chilly room heated by an old coke-fed stove, proved that fermentation was a living, vital process in which living organisms (bacteria) took part. Meanwhile, he entered into battle against the advocates of Spontaneous Generation, and, after a series of dramatic confrontations and experiments, finally compelled the French Academy of Sciences to come around to his side. What he said was that there never had been any demonstrations that Spontaneous Generation was possible. A man of surpassing thoroughness, he made himself thoroughly ready for these great contests with his opponents and entered them profoundly confident of the rightness of his cause and the powers he possessed not only to present a case, but to win it.

At Pouilly-le-Fort near Melun, Pasteur demonstrated to the world that sheep inoculated with the anthrax germ would die but that those given a preventive vaccine before they were inoculated with the anthrax germ would survive. His greatest achievement was, perhaps, to treat by injections an Alsation boy, Joseph Meister, who had been bitten by a rabid dog. The boy did not contract the terrible disease. Neither did a second boy also bitten and similarly treated. We now know that rabies is caused by a virus which Pasteur never saw. He was guided by the effect it had on the rabbits and dogs he used as the subjects of his experiments.

The modern method of securing immunity from disease

by giving preventive vaccines rests on Pasteur's truly stupendous achievements with microscopes that any modern schoolchild would regard as dim and inadequate. Pasteur, according to his colleagues, had a wonderful pair of eyes, and spotted things that escaped other workers. Part of his secret was that he recorded daily, in a special notebook, details that to him appeared significant. Often, he would watch for long periods, silently. Although he drank in much, he had little to say at the end of these protracted vigils. His extraordinary powers of concentration, and of drawing intuitively the correct deductions from his observations, gave him uncanny insight into the behavior of microbes and sharpened constantly his anticipation of their workings. He was thus able to sense acutely what he was looking for. Few men in the world's history have changed wholly the course of events in any field of activity. Pasteur's amazing originality made him one of those few.

But if Pasteur was the founder of modern medicine, and of the science of bacteriology, Robert Koch (1843–1910), the German country doctor from Wollstein, a small town in Posen, was the founder of modern bacteriological method. It is an odd coincidence that he too chose the anthrax germ for his investigations, largely because it was killing off sheep belonging to poor farmers in his neighborhood, who could ill afford to lose their livestock. He labored against heavy odds, with primitive equipment in a shed in his back garden. When he had completed his study of the anthrax germ, he sent it to Professor Ferdinand Cohn of Breslau, who summoned him to give a demonstration. While the demonstration was in progress Cohn sent out the word: "Drop everything. Go over at once to see Koch. This man has made a great discovery. . . ." He lost no time in publishing Koch's paper in his own journal. Koch was thus launched on a career that brought him international fame as a scientist.

Koch was a technical genius and his contributions to bacteriology were concerned with laboratory methods. He showed, for example, how microbes could be cultivated in a solid medium (nutrient gelatin) in order to facilitate their examination under the microscope. Pasteur's genius was of another sort — laboratory techniques were, to him, merely means to great ends. He is once said to have shocked a collaborator by his indifference to the shape of a germ.

As it happened, the English surgeon Joseph Lister (1827–1912), read one of Pasteur's essays on putrefaction which stated that fermentation was the work of microbes. Lister, who had vainly been seeking a way to prevent the infections that killed patients, in horrible manner, after the surgeons had finished operating, seized upon the clue in a visionary moment. He realized that infections during and after surgery were caused by microorganisms. So he began using carbolic acid as a disinfectant in the interest of "clean surgery," and saved the lives of many who had to undergo operations. Indirectly, therefore, "antisepsis" was the result of Pasteur's researches with the microscope, and the forerunner of the modern methods (asepsis) by which we prevent infections in surgery.

Part Four: 5

ULTRAMICROSCOPY made visible some of the larger viruses, but the smaller viruses did not come into view until the electron microscope had become a piece of laboratory equipment. It has been said that in fifteen years, electron microscopy extended human vision farther than ordinary microscopy had been able to extend it in three centuries. It has also been said that the electron microscope is as far in advance of the ordinary microscope as that instrument was in advance of the unaided human eye. Certainly, it is the electron microscope which has flung open the doors to both virology and molecular biology, two departments of science which have, in a few years, revolutionized our way of thinking about life and life's very beginnings.

But let us, for the moment, revert to the early days of virology. In about 1892, bacteriologists were using filters made of unglazed porcelain, or of natural earth of a certain kind, for the isolation of microbes. No organisms then known were able to pass through these filters, until the Russian botanist Dimitri Alexievitch Iwanowski found he could infect healthy tobacco plants with the organism which caused a plant disease (tobacco mosaic) *after* he had completed his filtering. Obviously, he had run across a microbe small enough to elude his filter. Next, Friedrich Loeffler (1852–1915), and Paul Frosch (1860–1928), who had both worked with Koch, found that foot-and-mouth disease, which affects livestock, was caused by a virus small enough to elude their filters. Thus, scientists became aware that both plants and animals could contract diseases caused by filterable viruses.

At this stage the larger viruses appeared to scientists as tiny dots. Barnard's ultraviolet microscope increased their visibility but, as we have said, only the electron microscope was able to reveal the smaller viruses. In order to throw these minute particles into greater relief, a technique of metal shadowing was evolved; they were coated with atoms of a suitable metal. The measurement of such tiny bodies also presented its difficulties, which were resolved ingeniously by the invention of membranes with pores of varying sizes. If a virus could pass through one of these membranes, then it had to be smaller than the size of the chosen pore.

A high-speed centrifuge was also employed to tell viruses from each other. When a bacteriologist wishes to force particles to sediment he uses a centrifuge which revolves his test tubes horizontally. Centrifugal force, overcoming the force of gravity, makes the particles settle. An ultra-, or high-speed, centrifuge whirls test tubes around even faster, and viral particles are forced down in relation to their size. With the aid of proper optical instruments, the researcher can keep track of the moving boundaries separating larger from smaller particles.

Viruses also had to be measured. Ultimately, a unit for their measurement was decided upon. It is called a millimicron (one-millionth of a millimeter), and it is generally written $m\mu$.

We can now see, and reproduce by means of photographs (electron micrography), images of living things that are not much larger than atoms themselves. We can photograph even the virus which causes poliomyelitis, one of the smallest of known microorganisms.

But the electron microscope is not the only apparatus available for the exploration of the "infinitesimally small." The story of how a "virtual microscope" came into being begins in the year 1895, when the German physicist Wilhelm Konrad Roentgen (1845–1923) was carrying out an experiment at Würzburg University, where he was a professor. He was passing cathode rays through a vacuum tube and watching the results. He had covered the tube with thick, black paper through which no ordinary light could pass; yet he noticed that a piece of "sensitized" paper lying on his bench showed certain marks. Since his "sensitized" paper could register the invisible rays of the spectrum, he assumed he had discovered some new sort of light. Roentgen had, of course, discovered X-rays, or Roentgen-rays, as they are called in his honor.

The next phase of the story takes place in 1912. Another German scientist, Max von Laue, found that X-rays could be diffracted by crystals, just like light. Indeed, objects as tiny as atoms could cause diffraction. The clear inference was that X-rays had a shorter wave length than light. During the 1920's, W. T. Astbury and others observed curious patterns whenever a piece of wool was examined under X-rays over a period of some hours. What were these curious patterns and how did they come to be there? The scientists concluded that X-ray beams had been reflected off the molecules of the wool-hair. Meanwhile, the British physicist Sir William Bragg (1862–1942), assisted by his son, Sir Laurence Bragg (b. 1890), measured the wave length of X-rays and calculated the arrangement of the atoms that make up crystals. For this, and other contributions on radioactivity, they shared the Nobel Prize.

The Braggs, father and son, had thrown fresh light on the nature of crystals and of molecular particles. When the crystallization of protein became possible, scientists realized that the structure of the protein molecule could be studied by means of X-ray analysis, and as time went on, they found themselves able to study life in its minutest forms with the aid of X-ray diffraction methods. The existence of various protein crystals means also that each type of molecule has its own shape. Nowadays, therefore, maps and models depict for us the arrangement of atoms in space.

X-ray crystallography has become a highly effective research tool in the hands of scientists. It offers what we have already named a "virtual microscope." By means of it, we are able to penetrate the interior of the cell, with its minute parts, in order to try to resolve the problems of heredity, with which the science of genetics is largely concerned. Even the subunits of cells have now been demonstrated to possess internal layer structures. But the most important effect of these exciting researches is that numerous molecular structures have been proved to exist. These structures, because they had never actually been seen, previously enjoyed a merely abstract validity. Now, no longer need they be regarded as hypothetical.

An Irish nobleman, Lord Rosse (1800–67), who was fascinated by the astronomical "marvels" revealed by Herschel and others, built an enormous telescope in Ireland. By means of this telescope, he detected, in 1845, that the nebula in the Constellation of the Hunting Dogs was a spiral "with two arms outstretched." His assistant, J. P. Nichol, in a book called *The Architecture of the Skies,* suggested that the spiral nebulae were universes like our own. Meanwhile, Louis Daguerre (1789–1851) and Nicéphore Niepce (1765–1839) had invented photography, which by 1839, had advanced so far as to provide both telescopy and microscopy with an invaluable asset. By the following year, the English-American John William Draper (1811–82) took the first photograph of the moon and gave celestial photography a beginning. Before long, the spectroscope, another asset to telescopy, enabled astronomers to see not only the outside of a star, but, so to speak, the "inside" of a star.

Newton, Wollaston, and Fraunhofer, had all perceived this possibility without ever being able to realize in some coherent practical device their theoretical knowledge of it. Fraunhofer happened to be examining with magnifying lens the solar spectrum which he had admitted through a fine aperture when he noticed that innumerable lines, not just the expected five, were to be seen covering the solar spectrum. He found the same effect when he studied the moon and Mars through a prism. Yet when he studied Castor he was confronted by three broad black bands. What did all this mean? Fraunhofer never quite supplied the answer. The man who did supply it was Gustav Kirchhoff (1824–87), professor of physics at Heidelberg, who had gone there to work with his bosom friend, a chemist named Robert Bunsen (1811–99). He directed, in turn, sunlight and the flame of any oxyhydrogen lamp, through a Bunsen burner before allowing them to play on a prism, sometimes dropping a little salt (sodium chloride) onto the flame of the Bunsen burner.

Whenever he used his pinch of salt he observed a bright orange band (*emission line of sodium*). Whenever he imposed his sodium flame on sunlight he observed that the solar spectrum dominated, dimming the orange band (*absorption line of sodium*). But, dark or light, he decided that his orange band signaled the presence of sodium. Helped by Robert Bunsen, he experimented with other substances, such as potassium and calcium, to find that each substance had its own particular spectrum. The spectrum of potassium was red and violet; that of calcium was violet, orange, and two yellows. On the strength of such information, it became clear from the solar spectrum that the sun contained sodium, iron, magnesium, and a number of substances with which we are perfectly familiar. Man is an inveterate maker of mysteries; the mysterious enthralls him. But science, which is knowledge, is a breaker of mysteries. Thus, out of the window went all those assumptions about the sun that imagination had helped to accumulate over the ages.

Once again it was only a beginning. It would not be too much to say that the true founder of spectroscopy was not so much Kirkhoff, who provided the means certainly, but a homely Englishman, Sir William Huggins (1824–1910), who, from his little observatory at Tulse Hill, London, identified in the spectra of stars the lines of sodium, iron, calcium, even hydrogen, and other substances. Thus, he was the pioneer of astrophysics, the department of science concerning itself with the material composition of heavenly bodies.

The discovery that the sun and other bodies contained substances we on earth knew well enough had the same sort of effect as the Cell Theory had had. The Cell Theory created an overwhelming sense of the oneness of life — of its essential integrity. Man was no longer special, or separate from the rest of creation; he was, biologically speaking, just another animal. In the same way, the revelations of astrophysics disposed of the feeling that the earth was special, that it had been created especially for Man. The whole universe seemed to consist of bodies very much like each other.

Auxiliary instruments, such as the spectroscope, and the increasing popularity of glass mirrors in reflector telescopes, changed even more dramatically our conceptions of space and its occupants. The celebrated American optician George William Ritchey, in 1918, completed grinding a 100-inch-diameter mirror for a reflecting telescope at Mount Wilson Observatory in America. At the same observatory with its magnificent equipment, an American, Harlow Shapley (b. 1885), journalist and zoologist turned astronomer, concentrated on globular clusters, almost all of which were to be seen in the southern hemisphere. About one hundred of them formed a smooth, luminous cloud. Why were they almost all in the southern hemisphere? Shapley reasoned that our solar system was, so to speak, "far to one side" of the universe taken in its entirety. The globular clusters were therefore visible chiefly to one side, in the direction of the southern hemisphere.

To cap it all, in 1927, the Dutchman Jan Hendrik Oort (b. 1900) discovered the rotation of the galaxy. The whole celestial system was in motion, wheeling around and around in conformity with Kepler's Laws. The nearer the center of rotation, the faster traveled the stars, and that center was somewhere in the neighborhood of Sagittarius, about 30,000 light years away from us. But what do we mean by the galaxy? The galaxy consists of all the stars we can actually see, estimated at some 30,000,000,000. Are we, then, really speaking of all space and all its inhabitants? Nobody can possibly tell for certain. On the other hand, not a soul would be surprised to hear of new worlds as yet beyond our reach.

In 1884, Huggins, using a telescope equipped with a spectroscope, caught a glimpse of a single green line when viewing a nebula in the Dragon. Did this mean the nebula consisted of gas? He tried the nebula of Orion and once again saw his single green line. Other investigations confirmed his opinion that these nebulae seemed to consist of gas. Edwin Hubble (b. 1889), the great American "conqueror of space," on the strength of his observations, declared space to be full of galactic nebulae spreading out in all directions. Born in Missouri, Hubble was educated at Chicago where his parents had moved. At the University of Chicago he fell under the influence of two brilliant instructors, Robert Millikan, who measured the charge of the atom, and George Ellery Hale, a brilliant practical astronomer.

Although Hubble was very taken by astronomy he did not immediately decide to make a vocation of it. Deferring to his father's wishes, he went to Oxford University and studied law. He was actually practicing his profession at Louisville, Kentucky, when he felt that the call to astronomy was no longer to be denied. He wrote to the Yerkes Observatory near Chicago, asking to be taken on to the staff. One other profession apart from astronomy, it has been said, lay open to him. As the possessor of a superb physique, he might have excelled as a heavyweight boxer. Hubble's decision to become an astronomer was taken shortly before America entered World War I. When America decided to participate he joined up and served in France. Upon his return home, he worked with his old mentor, G. E. Hale, at Mount Wilson, exploiting with profound, creative skill its wonderful 100-inch-diameter telescope. With this telescope he brought off his finest feats of astronomy.

Hubble had one great love: the galaxies. He could hardly keep his eyes off them, always with the thought of nature's essential integrity running through the back of his mind. He went on to demonstrate what Herschel, on the basis of inspired guesswork, had maintained. The spiral nebulae were systems outside the galaxy, reaching far out into space. In 1925, he showed how, apart from a few spiral nebulae, like that of Andromeda, the galaxies were all receding. The more distant they were, the faster they were receding.

Was the universe itself expanding? The English physicist Sir Arthur Eddington (1882–1944), thought it was, and so did several others, but the question remains without definite answer. To add a finishing touch, the Swiss scientist Fritz Zwicky, who was born (1898) in Bulgaria and worked in the United States, declared that the spiral nebulae, far from being dotted about in space just anyhow, in fact made definite combinations. It only needed Walter Baade, the German-American astronomer who was a native of Hamburg, to double the size of the universe (1952) and all the certainties of the past seemed rapidly to be ebbing away. The telescope had brought the comforts of a stability which had endured until the passing of the nineteenth century. A few tasks only, it once seemed, were left to astronomers, a matter of a little clearing up. Instead, came the shocks of our own century, carrying the same sort of impact as the pronouncements of Copernicus and Galileo must, in their day, have had.

We are now very remote from the old classical conception of a static, geocentric universe. Today radio telescopes are picking up signals from hydrogen clouds and stars, and astronomers are busy trying to interpret what they mean. Giant radio telescopes, like the one at Jodrell Bank near Manchester in northern England, track space vehicles as, laden with instruments, they propel themselves far, far beyond the earth's "envelope," relaying back to us the history of their flights. Important among the pieces of apparatus carried by these craft is the television camera, born of the knowledge that light could be turned into its electrical counterpart. The television camera, one of the new ways of extending Man's powers of vision, can "look" closely at the moon and at any other heavenly bodies which may become accessible, and reel off pictures that we on earth can pick up and study. With these, we can build up our ideas of what the worlds in space are really like.

Ever since Galileo's day a process of down-grading has continued remorselessly. The earth was the center of all and Man was God's "special creation." Only the saints and the angels and God himself were placed above Man in the great Ladder of Being which our forerunners of the Middle Ages accepted as unchangeable fact. The telescope, and the microscope, our capacity to see near and see far, have been largely responsible for establishing that Man is, after all, just another of the animals; that the earth, far from being unique, is just another planet, and that the sun is just one of numberless such suns. Indeed, we occupy a rather insignificant place, somewhere on the fringes of the incredible whole.

Yet consciousness of our diminished position seems hardly to matter. The realities that have ousted, and are ousting, the old, imaginary concepts, strike us as more wonderful than all the myths we once cherished. We sit back eagerly to await whatever each new day will bring forth.

Selected Reading List

Allen, Roy, *The Microscope*. Princeton, Van Nostrand, 1958.

Bailey, K. V., *Telescopes and Observations*. London, Muller, 1960.

Bell, Louis, *The Telescope*. New York, McGraw-Hill, 1962.

Bernal, J. D., *Science in History*. London, C. A. Watts, 1965.

Boas, Marie, *The Scientific Renaissance, 1450–1630*. New York, Harper & Row, 1962.

Bouwers, A., *Achievements in Optics*. New York, Elsevier Pub. Co., 1946.

Carpenter, W. B., and Dallinger, W. H., *The Microscope and Its Revelations*. London, Churchill, 1957.

Clason, Clyde, *Men, Planets and Stars*. New York, Putnam, 1956.

Cosslett, V. E., *The Electron Microscope*. London, Sigma, 1947.

Ditchburn, R. W., *Light*. New York, Interscience, 1958.

Doig, P., *A Concise History of Astronomy*. London, Chapman & Hall, 1960.

Gabor, D., *The Electron Microscope*. London, Electronics Engineering, 1954.

Guthrie, Douglas, *A History of Modern Medicine*. Philadelphia, Lippincott, 1958.

Hall, A. Rupert, *From Galileo to Newton, 1630–1720*. New York, Harper & Row, 1963.

Martin, C. N., *Thirteen Steps to the Atom*. New York, F. Watts, 1959.

Mason, S. F., *A History of the Sciences*. New York, Collier Books, 1962.

Rousseau, Pierre, *Man's Conquest of the Stars*. New York, Norton, 1961.

Singer, Charles, *A History of Biology*. New York, Abelard-Schuman, 1959.

Twyman, F., *Prism and Lens-making*. London, Hilger & Watts, 1955.

Index

Abbe, Ernst, 152
Abul-Wefa, 61
Adams, John Couch, 138, 140
Airy, George Bidell, 138
Al Battani, 60, 61
Alberti, Leon Battista, 29-31
Alexander, Brother, of Spina, 25, 26
Alfonso X, King, of Castille, 53
Althazen, 21, 22, 24, 27, 59
Amici, Giovanni Battista, 151
Andromeda, 44, 133, 185
Appleton, Sir Edward, 159, 160
Aquinas, Thomas, 49
Arago, François, 137
Archimedes of Syracuse, 18, 101
Aristarchus of Samos, 35
Aristotle, 23, 24, 40, 45, 48, 50, 118, 119
Armati, Salvino degli, 25, 26
Astbury, W. T., 179
Auzout, Adrien, 82

Baade, Walter, 185
Bacon, Roger, 24, 25
Barasino, Tomasso, 26
Barbaro, Daniello, 30
Barnard, Joseph Edwin, 154, 177
Barnett, M. A. F., 160
Barrow, Isaac, 99
Bass, George, 140
Bassi, Augustino, 172
Bauer, Ferdinand Lucas, 170
Bennett, John Hughes, 171
Bernal, Professor J. D., 9, 10, 102, 103, 122
Bernouilli, brothers, 128
Bichat, Marie François Xavier, 169
Bismarck, Chancellor, 171
Boerhaave, Hermann, 121
Bontemps, George, 142
Boreel, William, 33
Borelli, Giovanni Alfonso, 98, 118
Boul, Pierre, 89
Bouvard, Alexis, 136
Boyle, Robert, 98, 122
Bragg, Sir Laurence, 179
Bragg, Sir William, 179
Brahe, Tycho, 52-56
Brewster, Sir David, 151
Bright, G., 160
Brouncker, Lord, 123
Brown, Robert, 170
Brunelleschi, Filippo, 29, 30
Bunsen, Robert, 181
Busch, Hans, 155

Caesar, Julius, 9, 28
Callisto, 41
Cardon, Girolamo, 30
Cassini, Giovanni Domenico, 77, 87, 89-91, 103, 127
Castor, 132, 133, 181
Cauchois, 143
Charles II, 123
Châtelet, Madame du, 103
Christina, Queen, of Sweden, 73
Clairaut, Alexis, 128, 129, 141
Clarke, Alvan C., 143, 145
Clement IV, Pope, 24
Clement, William, 84
Cleopatra, 14
Cock, Christopher, 69
Cohn, Professor Ferdinand, 174
Colbert, Jean-Baptiste, 77, 78
Copernicus, Nicolaus, 35, 37, 41, 51, 52, 77, 97, 185
Culpepper, Edmund, 108

Daguerre, Louis, 180
d'Alembert, Jean, 128, 141
Darwin, Charles, 43, 103, 128, 168, 169

da Vinci, Leonardo, 29, 30, 108, 109
Dawes, 143
de Broglie, Louis, 155
Dee, John, 31
de Forest, 157
de Graaf, Regnier, 121
Della Porta, Giambattista, 30-33
Democritus, 49, 50
Descartes, René, 34, 69, 71-74, 76, 85, 91, 94, 95, 101, 103, 126
Digges, Leonard, 31
Dione, 90
Divini, Eustachio, 69
Dollond, John, 139-141
Dragon, the, 184
Draper, John William, 180
Drebbel, Cornelius, 33, 34
Driest, E., 156
Dujardin, Felix, 170
Bumortier, Barthelmy Charles, 170

Earth, 32, 35, 40, 41, 78-80, 89, 90, 126, 182, 186
Eddington, Sir Arthur, 185
Edison, Thomas Alva, 157, 158
Einstein, Albert, 155
Elizabeth I, Queen, 98
Euclid, 16-18, 24, 27, 103
Euler, Leonhard, 128
Europa, 41

Fabricius, Johann, 42
Fabrizio, Geronimo, 31
Faraday, Michael, 122, 148
Fermat, Pierre, 73, 91, 95, 96, 101
Flamsteed, John, 80, 90
Fontana, Felice, 170
Fracastorius of Verona, 31
Fraunhofer, Joseph von, 142, 143, 181
Fresnel, Augustin Jean, 147
Frosch, Paul, 177

Galilei, Galileo, 37, 39-41, 43-47, 49-51, 57, 63-65, 69, 80, 84, 97, 126, 129, 138, 185, 186
Galle, Johann, Gottfried, 138
Ganymede, 41
Gascoigne, William, 82
Gassendi, Abbé, 49, 50
Gemini, 130
George III, 131
Gilbert, William, 98
Giordano, Friar, of Pisa, 25
Glauber, Johann Rudolph, 67
Gordon, Bernard, 25
Grew, Nehemiah, 169
Grimaldi, Francesco, 76, 77, 95
Grosseteste, Robert, Bishop of Lincoln, 23
Guinand, Pierre Louis, 141, 142, 144

Hale, George Ellery, 184
Hall, Chester Moor, 139-141
Halley, Edmund, 80, 81, 97, 98, 100-102, 129
Hamilton, W. R., 154, 155
Harvey, William, 117, 118
Heaviside, Sir Oliver, 160
Henle, Friedrich Gustave Jakob, 170
Hercules, 133
Hero of Alexandria, 17
Herschel, Caroline, 132
Herschel, William, 129-136, 138, 149, 154, 180, 185
Hertz, Heinrich, 148, 157
Hevelius (Höwelke), Johannes, 80, 81, 108, 109
Hipparchus, 35, 60
Hofnagel, Georg, 106, 107
Hooke, Robert, 67, 69, 70, 76, 82, 84, 92, 94, 97, 98, 101, 102, 108, 122-125, 168, 169
Hooker, 145
Hubble, Edwin, 184, 185
Huggins, Sir William, 182, 184
Huygens, Christiaan, 34, 69, 77, 80, 84-87, 89-92, 94, 95, 103, 109, 134, 139, 146
Huygens, Constantijn, 86, 87

Iapetus, 90
Io, 41
Ives, F. E., 152

Iwanowski, Dimitri Alexievitch, 177

James I, 33
Jansen, Johannes, 32-34
Jansen, Zacharias, 33, 39
Jupiter, 41, 78, 79, 136, 137

Kant, Immanuel, 134, 135
Kepler, Johannes, 22, 54-58, 60, 62-64, 97, 132, 138, 183
Kircher, Athanasius, 107
Kirchoff, Gustav, 181, 182
Klingenstierna, Samuel, 141
Koch, Robert, 174, 175, 177
Krause, F., 156

Lagrange, Joseph Louis, 128
Lambert, Johann, 132
Laplace, Pierre Simon, 128, 129, 137, 155
Le Bas, 89
Leibniz, Gottfried Wilhelm, 101, 103
Leo XIII, Pope, 49
Le Verrier, Urbain-Jean-Joseph, 137, 138, 140
Lick, James, 145
Lippershey, Jan, 32
Lister, Joseph, 151, 175
Lister, Joseph Jackson, 151
Loeffler, Friedrich, 177
Louis XIV, 77
Louis XVI, 128

Maestline, Michael, 54
Magnus, Albertus, 24
Malapert, Charles, 44
Malpighi, Marcello, 117-119, 123, 169
Mänsson, Peder, 66
Marconi, Guglielmo, 158, 159
Mars, 89, 181
Marton, L., 156
Maupertuis, Pierre Louis de, 95, 96, 103
Maurice, Prince, of Nassau, 72
Maurolico, Francesco, 30, 31
Mayer (Marius), Simon, 44, 133
Maxwell, James Clerk, 148, 149, 154, 157
Meister, Joseph, 173
Mercury, 44, 49
Messier, Charles, 133
Metius (Jakob Andrianzoon of Alkmaar), 32, 34
microscopes, 12, 13, 27, 33, 34, 51, 61-64, 106-108, 110-115, 118, 121-127, 131, 150, 151, 154, 156, 157, 167, 168, 173-178
Milky Way, The, 41, 134, 135
Millikan, Robert, 184
Mohl, Hugo, 170
moon, the, 40, 60, 71, 181
Morse, S. F. B., 159
Müller, H. O., 156
Muller, Johannes, 170
Müller, Otto Friedrich, 172

Napier, John, 60
Napoleon, 128, 147
Needham, J. T., 116
Neptune (Planet X), 136-138
Newton, Isaac, 64, 69, 76, 80, 92-95, 97-106, 109, 122, 126-128, 131, 132, 139, 146, 157, 181
Nichol, J. P., 180
Nicholas, Cardinal of Cusa, 26, 30
Niepce, Nicéphore, 180

Octavian, 14
Oort, Jan Hendrik, 183
Orange, Prince of, 85
Orion, 41, 44, 130, 133, 184
Orleans, Cherubin, 107

Pantheus, J. A., 67
Pasteur, Louis, 112, 116, 119, 128, 168, 172-175
Peiresc, Nicolas Fabri de, 44, 133
Pepys, 123
Picard, Abbé Jean, 77, 78, 80, 81
Planck, Max, 155
Plato, 50
Pleiades, the, 41

Pliny The Elder, 14
Pollux, 133
Power, Henry, 167-169
Ptolemaius, Claudius (Ptolemy), 16-18, 20-22, 24, 27, 35, 37, 45
Ptolemy (Claudius Ptolemaius), 16-18, 20-22, 24, 27, 35, 37, 45

Redi, Francesco, 116
Rhea, 90
Rheinhold, Erasmus, 53
Riccioli, Giambaptista, 90
Ritchey, George William, 183
Ritter, Johann Wilhelm, 149, 150, 154
Roemer, Ole, 77-82, 91
Roentgen, Wilhelm Konrad, 178-179
Rokitansky, Karl von, 171
Rosse, Lord, 180
Rudolf II, Emperor, 56
Ruzcka, Ernst, 156

Sagittarius, 133, 183
Saturn, 40, 41, 86, 90, 131, 136-138
Scheiner, Christopher, 42, 57, 63, 64, 107
Schleiden, Matthias Jakob, 113, 168-170
Schönlein, Johann Lucas, 172
Schott, 152
Schrödinger, Erwin, 155
Schwann, Theodor, 113, 168-171
Schyrle (Schyrlaeus) of Rheita, 64
Shapley, Harlow, 183
Short, James, 130
Snellius (Snell), Willebrord, 60, 61, 74, 76
Spallanzani, Lazarro, 116
Spencer, Charles A., 150, 152
Spencer, Herbert R., 150
Stelluti, Francesco, 107
Stevin, Simon, 60
Strabo, 14
sun, 35, 40, 41, 44, 49, 52, 60, 78, 90, 98, 131, 132, 134, 136-138, 182, 186
Swammerdam, Jan, 120, 121, 126

telescopes, 12, 31-34, 39-41, 43, 51, 53, 62-64, 66, 69, 70, 81, 82, 86, 87, 89, 90, 92, 106, 108, 114, 125-127, 129-131, 133-136, 138, 139, 150, 168, 180, 183-186
Tethys, 90
Thomson, Sir J. J., 157, 158
Titan, 86
Tolles, Robert B., 150, 152
Torrecelli, Evangelista, 65
Triffid, 133
Tuve, M. A., 160

universe, the, 12, 24, 35, 44, 51, 56, 73, 131, 133, 134, 136, 182, 183, 186
Uranus, 131, 136-138

van Leeuwenhoek, Anthony, 69, 110-119, 124, 125, 172
Vanoccio, 67
Venus, 40, 44
Vieta, 60
Virchow, Rudolf, 171
Vitello, 22, 27
Voltaire, 103, 104
von Baer, Karl, 121
Von Laue, Max, 179
von Liebig, Justus, 173
von Wallenstein, Duke Albrecht, 56

Wagner, Rudolf, 170
Watson-Watt, Sir Robert, 163
Wenham, Francis, 151
Wollaston, Francis, 146, 181
Wren, Christopher, 97, 101, 123
Wright, Thomas, 134, 135

Yerkes, Charles T., 145
Young, Thomas, 146, 147

Zeiss, Carl, 152
Zernike, Fritz, 152
Zucchi, Nicola, 64, 66
Zwicky, Fritz, 185

The Author

L. J. Ludovici's interest in science dates back to his school days. His early education was in Ceylon, his birthplace, but he went to England to attend Oxford University. For many years he was active in book publishing and founded a firm of which he was literary director. In 1954 he decided to devote his full time to writing. He makes his home in England, where he is a widely known author for both adults and young people. SEEING NEAR AND SEEING FAR is Mr. Ludovici's fifth book in Putnam's Science Survey Series.

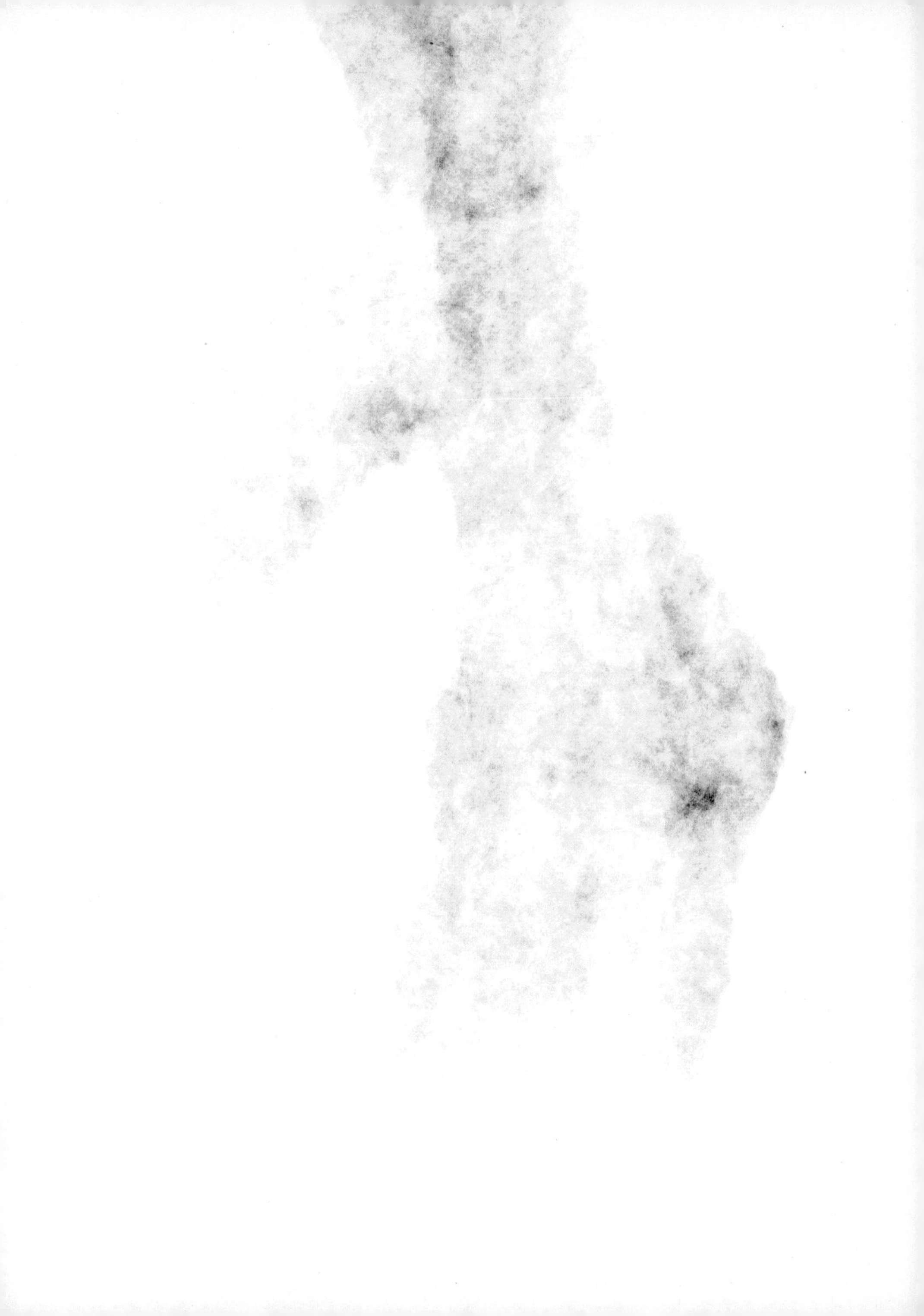

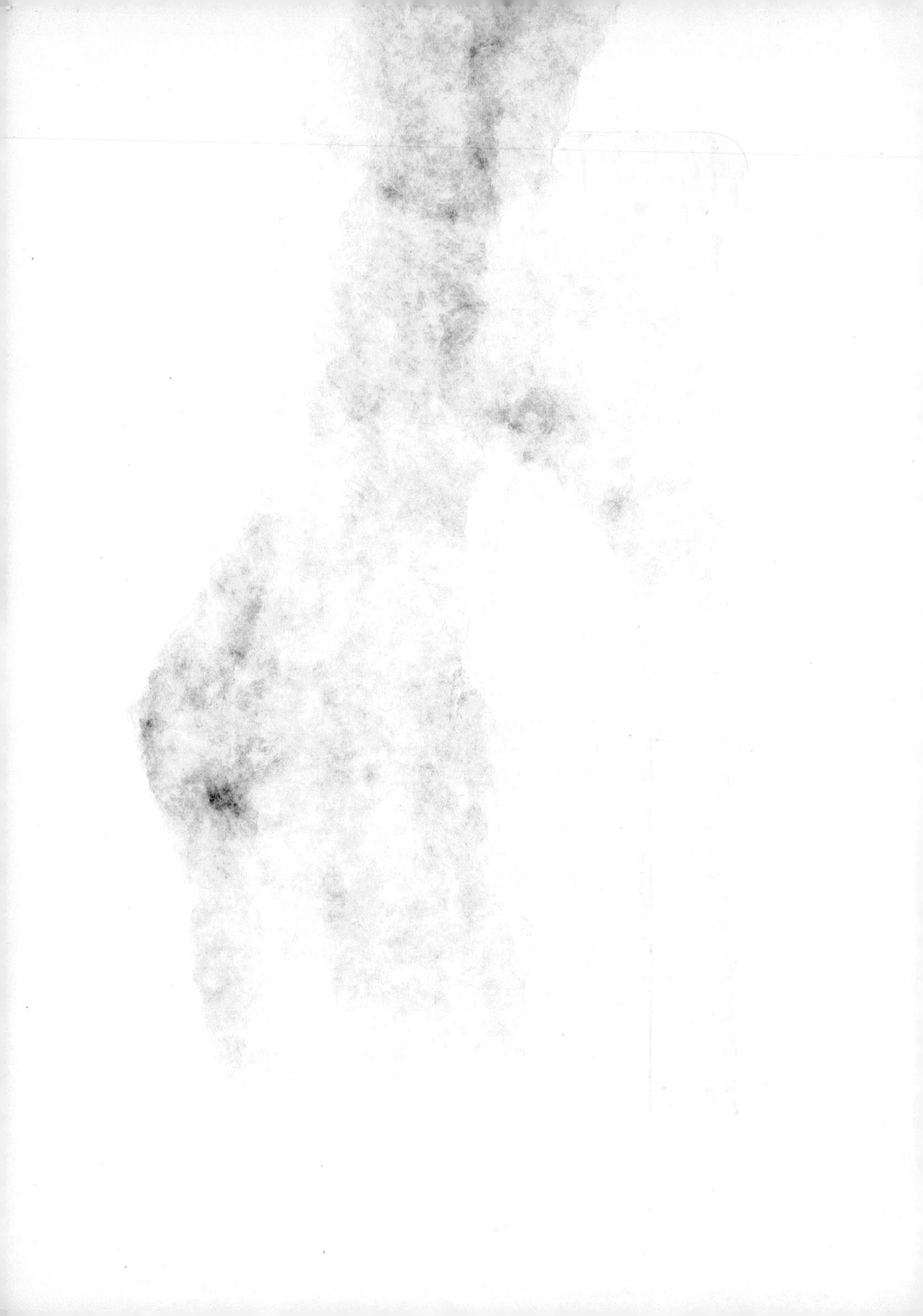